D0876259

Methuen's Monographs on Physical Subjects
General Editor: B. L. Worsnop, B.Sc., Ph.D.

X-RAY CRYSTALLOGRAPHY

X-RAY CRYSTALLOGRAPHY

by

R. W. JAMES

F.R.S.

EMERITUS PROFESSOR OF PHYSICS IN THE UNIVERSITY OF CAPE TOWN

WITH A GENERAL PREFACE BY

O. W. RICHARDSON

F.R.S.

YARROW RESEARCH PROFESSOR OF THE ROYAL SOCIETY
NOBEL LAUREATE IN PHYSICS, 1928

WITH 29 DIAGRAMS

LONDON: METHUEN & CO. LTD.
NEW YORK: JOHN WILEY & SONS, INC.

First Published June 12th 1930
Second Edition September 1941
Third Edition December 1945
Fourth Edition February 1950
Fifth Edition 1953
Reprinted 1957
Reprinted with minor corrections 1961
Reprinted 1965

5.4
CATALOGUE NO. 12/4037/66

PRINTED IN GREAT BRITAIN BY
BUTLER AND TANNER LTD., FROME AND LONDON

GENERAL PREFACE

THIS series of small monographs is one which should commend itself to a wide field of readers.

The reader will find in these volumes an up-to-date résumé of the developments in the subjects considered. The references to the standard works and to recent papers will enable him to pursue further those subjects which he finds of especial interest. The monographs should therefore be of great service to physics students who have examinations to consider, to those who are engaged in research in other branches of physics and allied sciences, and to the large number of science masters and others interested in the development of physical science who are no longer in close contact with recent work.

From a consideration of the list of authors it is clear that the reader need have no doubt of the accuracy of the general accounts found in these volumes.

O. W. RICHARDSON

KING'S COLLEGE
LONDON

PREFACE

IN this book I have tried to give an outline of the main principles underlying the methods of analysing crystals by means of X rays, which may be of interest, as a general account, to students of other branches of physics, and at the same time serve as an introduction to the subject for those about to take up its study seriously. Detailed examples of the analysis of simple crystals are now to be found in a number of text-books, and an adequate treatment of more complicated cases would have been impossible in the somewhat limited space at my disposal. I have thought it better, therefore, to deal on the whole with general methods rather than with their application to particular cases, hoping that the account given may stimulate the reader to consult the original sources.

My indebtedness to many other works will be plain, and reference is made to some of them in the Bibliography. All writers on this subject must in particular owe much to *X-Rays and Crystal Structure*, by W. H. and W. L. Bragg, to Ewald's admirable book *Kristalle und Röntgenstrahlen*, and to Niggli's *Geometrische Kristallographie des Diskontinuums*. My thanks are due to Professor W. L. Bragg, F.R.S., who kindly read the manuscript and made a number of valuable suggestions; to Mr. Herbert Bell, M.A., through whose criticisms certain obscurities have been, I hope, removed; and to the Royal Society for permission to reproduce Fig. 28, which was first published in their Proceedings.

R. W. J.

PHYSICAL LABORATORIES
THE UNIVERSITY OF MANCHESTER
March, 1930

PREFACE TO THE FIFTH EDITION

IN preparing the fifth edition I have tried so far as possible to preserve the method of presentation of the earlier editions, which experience has shown to have been of value to many students beginning work on the subject, who have wished to obtain a general idea, not overloaded with technical detail, of the methods and principles of structure determination.

The alterations in the first four chapters are mainly those made necessary by variations in technique, and by changes of emphasis, that have occurred since the book was first written. A chapter dealing with the determination of atomic parameters, the use of Fourier series, the refinement of the results obtained by them, and the determination of phases has been added.

I should like to thank the Cambridge University Press for permission to include Fig. 26 from *Acta Crystallographica*.

R. W. J.

UNIVERSITY OF CAPE TOWN
March, 1952

NOTE TO 1961 EDITION

VERY few alterations have been made in this edition. The last section of Chapter VI has been modified to include a necessarily brief account of some of the recent work on biologically important structures, but, apart from this, only minor changes have been made.

R. W. J.

CAPE TOWN
June, 1960

CONTENTS

CHAPTER I

CRYSTAL FORM AND THE SPACE-LATTICE

INTRODUCTION

THE regular geometrical form of a crystal is a consequence of the regular arrangement of the molecules of which it is built up. The regularity is that of a 3-dimensional pattern, in which a certain unit of structure is repeated over and over again in space, just as the regularity of a wall-paper is due to the repetition of a certain design in two dimensions. It had long been recognized that a theory of this type would account for the observed facts of crystalline form and symmetry, and the geometry of such space-patterns had been fully worked out, but it was not until the development of X-ray crystallography that it became possible to determine the actual nature of the unit, and of the pattern in any crystal. It was in 1912 that v. Laue pointed out that a crystal might be expected to diffract X rays. The first diffraction patterns from crystals were obtained in the same year by Friedrich and Knipping, and the first analyses of crystal structures were published by W. L. Bragg shortly afterwards. At first, only the simplest structures could be analysed, but great advances in technique have been made since those early days, and it has been possible to determine in detail the arrangement of the atoms in many quite complicated molecules. The study of crystal structure has become an important part of the physics of the solid state, and from relatively simple beginnings a large and important science has developed. X-ray crystallography is descended from, and constantly uses, the results of the older crystallography, and it will therefore be necessary at the outset to deal briefly with a few of the more important principles of the parent science.

GENERAL PROPERTIES OF CRYSTALS

A single crystal is homogeneous, in the sense that it has identical properties at all points within it; it is not in general, however, isotropic; that is to say, that directed properties, such as thermal or electrical conductivity, or the coefficient of thermal expansion, or the velocity of propagation of light within the crystal, depend upon the direction in the crystal which is being considered. Parallel to any given direction, the properties at all points in the crystal are the same, but, at any one point, the same property differs in different directions. This suggests at once a regularity in the internal structure of the crystal, for, if the arrangement of its constituent molecules were entirely at random, it is clear that we could not have such a dependence of properties on direction. It is this internal regularity of structure that is the essential characteristic of the crystalline state, and not the external regularity of form: the latter, however, is a direct consequence of the former, and from it we may get the first hint as to the nature of the internal structure.

CRYSTAL FORM AND THE LAW OF RATIONAL INDICES

Before proceeding further, it is desirable to give greater precision to the idea of crystal form. Let us consider, for example, what is meant by the statement that potash alum crystallizes in regular octahedra. It is true that a crystal of alum may grow in such a way that its bounding faces do form a regular octahedron, but, unless special precautions are taken, the crystal will probably have eight faces of different sizes, and may not at first sight bear any resemblance to a regular octahedron. The essential point is that whatever the relative sizes of the faces, and whatever the actual shape of the crystal, the angles between the faces are always those between the faces of a regular octahedron. Or, to put it in another way, the crystal may always be set so that its eight faces are parallel to those of a regular octahedron.

It is thus the directions of the faces and not the shape of the crystal which is the essential matter. From any point within a crystal let perpendiculars be drawn to the faces, supposed produced if necessary. The radiating bundle of normals so obtained is independent of the size and shape of the faces, and depends only on their directions; it is thus characteristic of the form of a crystal on which a certain set of faces is developed, and is a much better description of it than its actual shape would be, since this depends so greatly on the accidents of growth. We may if we like suppose a sphere described about the origin of the normals, and intersecting them in a set of points which will again be independent of all but the directions of the faces. When a crystallographer speaks of the geometrical form of a crystal, it is really this radiating set of normals, or the corresponding array of points on the sphere, which he has in mind.

The eight faces corresponding to the octahedron are said to constitute a **form.** A crystal may have more than one form developed at the same time: an alum crystal might, for example, have six faces corresponding to those of a cube, as well as the octahedral faces: but, for the same crystal, the relative directions of the faces of the different forms are fixed, and very definite rules, which we must now consider, govern the directions which are possible.

It is first of all necessary to choose a set of axes, fixed in the crystal, to which the directions of the faces can be referred, and, for this purpose, three lines parallel to the lines of intersection of three faces that do not lie in the same plane are used. In theory, any three such faces will serve, but in practice there is usually some set of axes which suggests itself as the most convenient. In a cubic crystal, for example, three edges of the cube, giving a set of rectangular axes, would always be chosen.

Three faces thus define the axes; we must now take a fourth face, which must cut all three axes, as a standard plane. Let ABC (Fig. 1) be such a plane, and let it make intercepts OA ($=a$), OB ($=b$), OC ($=c$), on the axes Ox, Oy, Oz, respectively. The experimental law which is found to govern the directions of the other faces of the crystal can now be stated as follows:

A face which is parallel to a plane whose intercepts on the three axes are Ha, Kb, Lc, where H, K, and L are

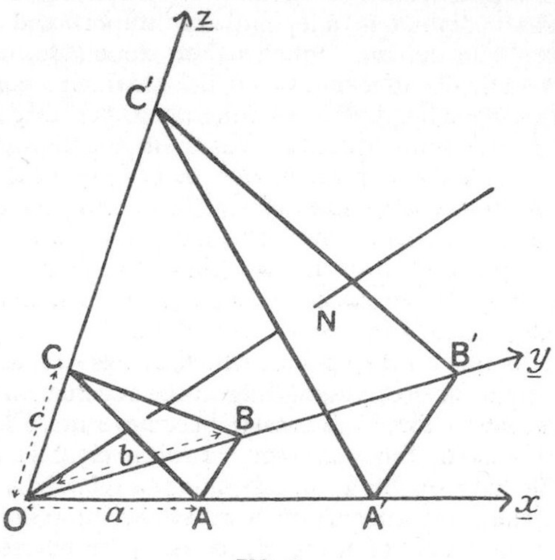

FIG. 1

whole numbers, is a possible face of the crystal, and for the planes which commonly occur, *H*, *K*, and *L* are small whole numbers.

For all planes parallel to a given direction, the **ratio** of the intercepts on the axes is the same, so that if $A'B'C'$ be a possible crystal face, we have, from the rule given above,

$$OA':OB':OC'=Ha:Kb:Lc$$
$$=a/KL:b/LH:c/HK=a/h:b/k:c/l, \quad (1)$$

where *h*, *k*, *l*, are again small whole numbers. The numbers *h*, *k*, *l*, define the plane, to which a symbol (*hkl*) may be given, and are called its Miller indices, after Miller who introduced them. The Miller indices are always whole numbers, and for the commonly occurring faces of a crystal, small whole numbers, and the law which we have just considered is known as the **Law of Rational Indices.**

For a given value of the ratio $a:b:c$, the Miller indices of a plane are inversely proportional to its intercepts on the axes. The geometrical reason for using them rather than the numbers H, K, L, which are directly proportional to the intercepts, is that h/a, k/b, l/c, are proportional to the direction cosines of the normal to the plane (hkl), and, as we have seen, it is the normal to the plane which is used to define it crystallographically. The proportionality follows at once from equation (1), for if λ, μ, ν are the direction cosines of the normals to the plane $A'B'C'$ (Fig. 1), that is to say the cosines of the angles which the normal makes with the axes of x, y, and z respectively, and p is the length of the perpendicular, ON, from the origin of the plane, we have $p=\lambda.\ OA'=\mu.\ OB'=\nu.\ OC'$, and hence, from equation (1), $\lambda : \mu : \nu = h/a : k/b : l/c$.

There is the further advantage that when a plane is parallel to one of the axes, and the corresponding intercept becomes infinite, the Miller index becomes zero. The ratio $a{:}b{:}c$ is known as the axial ratio of the crystal. In purely crystallographic work, b is usually made equal to unity, a and c being then in general not integers. The value of the axial ratio depends upon the choice of the standard plane, and is thus to some extent arbitrary. We shall find later, however, that a physical interpretation can be given to the numbers a, b, c, and that this arbitrariness will in some degree disappear.

The indices of the standard plane are always (111): in giving those of the other planes it is customary to express them so that they contain no common factor. In the case of the alum crystal considered above we shall take the axes parallel to the intersections of the cube faces. One of the octahedral faces will then be taken as the standard plane; its indices will be (111), and, since it makes equal intercepts on the three axes, we have $a=b=c$. The face of the octahedron opposite to that chosen as standard will, if the origin is chosen within the crystal, make negative intercepts on all three axes, or, more generally, the direction cosines of its normals will all be negative. The indices are therefore negative, and the symbol of the face is written $(\bar{1}\,\bar{1}\,\bar{1})$, the negative sign, for the sake of compactness, being put above the corresponding figure. The symbols of the eight faces of the octahedron are $(1\,1\,1)$, $(1\,\bar{1}\,1)$, $(\bar{1}\,1\,1)$, $(\bar{1}\,\bar{1}\,1)$, $(1\,\bar{1}\,\bar{1})$, $(1\,1\,\bar{1})$, $(\bar{1}\,1\,\bar{1})$,

$(\bar{1}\,\bar{1}\,\bar{1})$, and the symbol for the whole set of faces, or the *form*, is $\{1\,1\,1\}$. In a similar way, the symbol for the cube form is $\{100\}$ and that for the set of twelve planes containing an axis and a cube diagonal, the dodecahedral form, is $\{110\}$. One zero always occurs in the symbol for a face which is parallel to an axis, and two occur in that for one which is parallel to one of the axial planes.

THE LAW OF RATIONAL INDICES AND THE SPACE-LATTICE

The law of rational indices follows very simply if we assume the crystal to be built up by stacking identical units in a 3-dimensional pattern. Such a pattern will possess the homogeneity which we have seen to be one of the principal characteristics of a crystal, for each unit is similar and similarly situated, and, if we suppose the extension of the pattern to be infinite, no unit is in any way to be distinguished from any other.

It will be easiest first of all to consider a pattern in two dimensions, such as a wall-paper pattern. Its essential characteristic is that it is produced by continued repetition of a single 'unit', and that, in the completed pattern, such units must lie in rows, equally spaced, so that corresponding points of the units lie at the points of intersection of two sets of equally spaced parallel lines. For, since all the units are to be identical and identically placed, if a point in one unit, A_{10} in Fig. 2, lies in a certain direction, and at a certain distance a, from a corresponding point A_{00} in another unit, there must be a corresponding point A_{20} in the same direction and at the same distance from A_{10}, and so on indefinitely in both directions. Thus $A_{00}A_{10}A_{20}$ . . . lie in the same straight line, and $A_{00}A_{10}=A_{10}A_{20}=A_{20}A_{30}$ . . . $=a$. Similarly, if in any other direction from A_{00} there is a point A_{01} at a distance b, there must be other points, A_{02}, A_{03} . . . collinear with A_{00} and A_{01} and equally spaced. Moreover, there must be rows of points along lines passing through A_{10}, A_{20}, A_{30} . . . parallel to the row $A_{00}A_{01}A_{02}$ . . . and with exactly the same spacing, b. Thus the collection of points taken altogether forms a regular mesh, or net-plane.

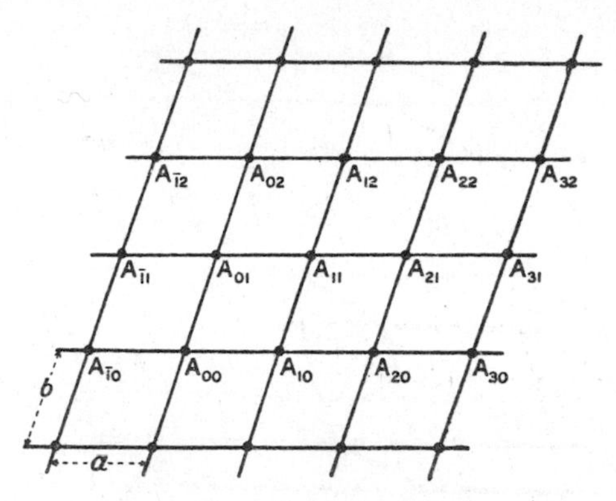

FIG. 2. Two-dimensional lattice

If we extend this idea to three dimensions, we shall have a row of points through A_{00} all equally spaced in some third direction, not in the same plane as A_{10} and A_{01}, and similar, parallel, rows of points through every one of the points in the original net-plane, the whole collection of points being formed by the intersections of three sets of parallel and equally spaced planes. Such a collection of points is called a **space-lattice.**

Fig. 3 represents a small part of such a space-lattice. We may take any point O as origin of co-ordinates, and take as axes three directions OA, OB, OC, which are the directions of three rows of points not lying in the same plane. Let A, B, C be the positions of three points adjacent to O, and such that no other points lie inside the parallelepiped of which OA $(=a)$, OB $(=b)$, and OC $(=c)$ are three edges. Such a parallelepiped is said to be a **unit cell** of the lattice, and the distances a, b, and c its **primitive translations.** The co-ordinates of any point of the lattice, referred to the origin and axes considered, are (ma, nb, pc) where m, n, p are any whole numbers positive or negative. The primitive translations of the lattice may be chosen in an indefinite number of ways. The corresponding unit cell will always have the same volume, although its shape will vary. The whole lattice may

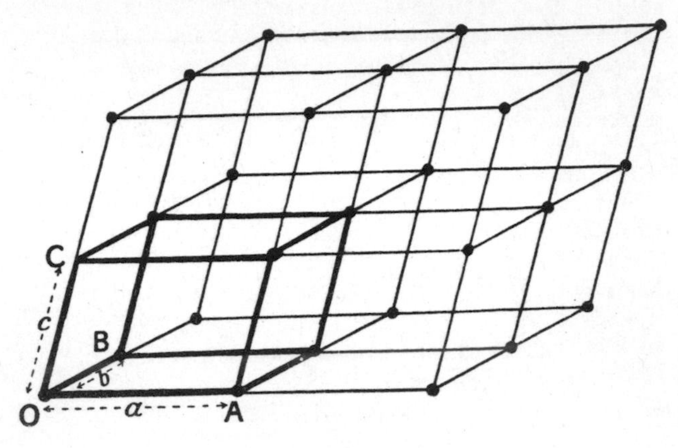

FIG. 3. Space-lattice

be built up by stacking together such unit cells, the lattice points lying at the common corners. There is **one** lattice point per unit cell, for, although the cell has eight corners, eight cells meet at each corner, and only an eighth of a point belongs to each cell.

THE LATTICE PLANES

In a space-lattice, all the points may be included in a set of parallel and equally spaced **planes,** each of which is a net-plane. Such a set of planes may be chosen in an indefinite number of ways; if each plane of the set is densely occupied by points, the planes will be widely spaced; if they are sparsely occupied, they will be close together. If we consider a crystal as formed of similar units arranged in a space-lattice, it will be seen that planes can be chosen in the crystal which contain a large number of units closely packed, and that these planes are comparatively widely separated. Such planes might well form the natural boundaries to the collection of units, in other words, the faces of the crystal. The more sparsely occupied planes have much less physical reality; they exist mathematically, but there is no reason to suppose that they will form crystal faces. We shall see that this idea leads at once to the law of rational indices.

For simplicity, we return to two dimensions. The analogues of the planes in the space-lattice are now rows of points. Let any two important directions, *OA*, *OB*, in Fig. 4, be chosen as axes, and let the primitive translations be *a* and *b*. Rows of points may be chosen in directions other than those of the axes, and we notice that their intercepts on the axes are always in the ratio of two integers, say *m* and *n*, and further, that the densely occupied rows are always those for which the ratio $m:n$ is a ratio of small whole numbers. Thus, if we assign indices to the rows analogous to the Miller indices for planes, which are proportional to the reciprocals of the intercepts of the rows on the axes, these indices will be small whole numbers for the principal rows.

Extending this once more to three dimensions, we see that the planes which contain a large number of lattice points per unit area are those whose intercepts on the axes are in the ratio of three small whole numbers *m*, *n*, *p*. That is to say, they are planes for which the law of rational indices holds.

It will be noticed that the rows of the set (2, 1) in Fig. 4 divide the *a* edge of each unit of the net into two equal parts and the *b* edge into one part. It is easy to see generally that rows of the set (m, n) divide the *a* edges into *m* parts and the *b* edges into *n* parts. This can be extended to three dimensions. The planes of the set (h, k, l) divide the *a*, *b*, and *c* edges of each unit cell into *h*, *k*, and *l* equal parts respectively. The indices *h*, *k*, and *l* must have no common factor. Every lattice point will then lie on one of the planes of the set, and all the planes will contain the same number of points.

The idea of the space-lattice as underlying the structure of crystals was first worked out in detail by Bravais many years ago. The unit of crystal structure, molecule or atom, or group of molecules or atoms, was supposed to lie at the point of a space-lattice, and the complete structure to be built up from the unit simply by applying to it over and over again the lattice translations. We must now see how the

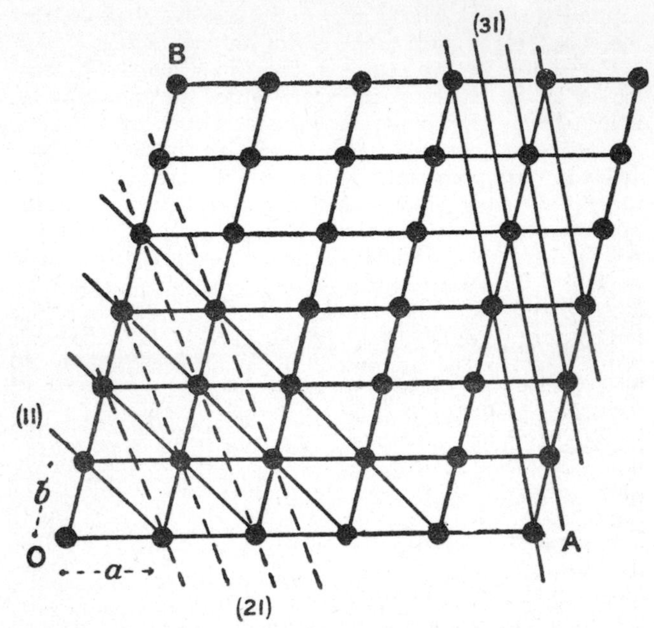

FIG. 4. Rows of points in a 2-dimensional lattice

application of X rays to the problem enables us to demonstrate the actual existence of these space patterns and to determine their arrangement.

CHAPTER II

THE CRYSTAL LATTICE AS A DIFFRACTION GRATING

INTRODUCTION

THE important discovery of von Laue which made it possible to investigate crystal structure by means of X rays was based directly on the idea of the crystal as a repeating pattern in space. It is well known that if a beam of light falls on a screen perforated with holes arranged in a regular pattern whose spacings are comparable with the wave-length of the light, diffraction occurs; the light, after passing through the screen, consists not only of a somewhat weakened beam in the direction of the incident light, but also of other, regularly arranged, separate beams, deviated from the original direction through angles depending on the ratio of the wave-length of the light to the spacings of the pattern. If both the wave-length and the scale of the pattern are diminished, so as to keep this ratio the same, the diffraction pattern, apart from changes in intensity, remains unaltered. The diffraction is due to the interaction of the regularly periodic pattern with the regularly periodic light waves.

If a crystal consists of the repetition of similar units in a regular pattern, we might perhaps expect to get diffraction when a beam of light is passed through it. The crystal pattern, however, repeats itself several thousand times in the length of a single light wave, and it is evident therefore that we cannot expect diffraction effects unless we can use light whose wave-length is several thousand times shorter than that of visible light. In 1912, when v. Laue made his discovery, it was not known for certain whether X rays were electromagnetic waves, but it was known that if they were, their wave-length must be about ten thousand times shorter than that of visible light. Laue therefore suggested to Friedrich and Knipping that they should try the effect of passing a beam of X rays through a crystal, allowing the transmitted beam to fall on a photographic plate. It was to be expected that the diffracted beams, if present, would be very weak compared with the directly transmitted beam. A long exposure was therefore given, and, when the plate was developed, the central spot due to the direct beam was found to be surrounded by a pattern of spots, arranged in a manner corresponding to the symmetry of the crystal, and plainly due to diffracted beams. Upon this simple but brilliant experiment the whole subject of X-ray crystallography is based. We may sum up its results by saying that a crystal is to be regarded, in so far as its action upon X rays is concerned, as a 3-dimensional diffraction grating. It will be necessary therefore to consider briefly the problem of diffraction by such a grating, and it will be convenient to base our discussion upon the more familiar problems in one and two dimensions which occur in ordinary optics.

DIFFRACTION BY GRATINGS OF ONE, TWO, AND THREE DIMENSIONS

Let us consider first of all the case of a screen perforated with a large number of small holes, A_0, A_1, A_2, ... (Fig. 5), equally spaced along a straight line. Upon this screen there falls a train of plane waves whose wave-length, λ, is of the same order as, but rather less than, the spacing, a, of the

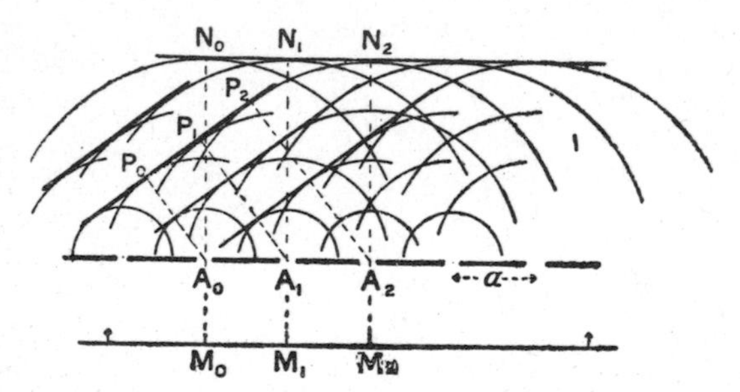

FIG. 5. Diffracted waves from a row of equally-spaced holes

holes. Each hole, under the action of the incident waves, becomes the centre of a set of spherical wavelets spreading out on the far side of the screen. If the waves are incident normally on the screen, so that a given wave-front reaches all the holes simultaneously, the corresponding spherical wavelets all start at the same instant. At any later time, therefore, they will all touch a cylinder, whose axis is the line of holes, which expands radially with the velocity of the waves, and this, by Huyghens' principle, is the resultant wave-front on the far side of the screen. There will of course be a cylindrical transmitted wave-front corresponding to each incident plane wave-front, the whole forming a train of cylindrical waves.

This wave train has the following important characteristic. The sum of the distances from any incident wave-front to a hole, and from the same hole to the cylindrical wave-front, is the same for all the holes. If $M_0M_1M_2$ ... is the trace of an incident wave-front, and $N_0N_1N_2$ ... the trace of one of the cylindrical wave-fronts in the plane of the diagram, $M_0A_0+A_0N_0=M_1A_1+A_1N_1=$ ... In other words, the difference between the paths by way of any two holes from an incident to a transmitted wave-front is zero. A wave of this kind is called a wave of **zero order.** Owing to the equality of path, the wavelets from all the holes agree in phase on the transmitted wave-front; it is, in fact, this agreement which makes it a wave-front.

Now if, as we have supposed, the holes are equally spaced, and if $a>\lambda$, it is easy to see that there will be other surfaces upon which the wavelets agree in phase, and hence, other transmitted waves. Imagine a conical surface, having $A_0A_1A_2$ as axis, of which $P_0P_1P_2$ ... is a trace, such that the path from the incident wave-front to it, by way of a hole, increases by one wave-length for each successive hole. Such a surface can be found if the holes are regularly spaced, but not otherwise. There will again be agreement of phase on this surface, for, if a crest of a wavelet from A_0 touches it, so will the crest emitted from A_1 one period earlier, and that emitted from A_2 two periods earlier, and so on. The conical surface is thus a possible wave-front, and we may call it the wave of the first order, since the path to it from any incident wave-front increases by *one* wave-length for each hole. In exactly the same way, other conical wave-fronts may be found for which the path difference from hole to hole is 2λ, 3λ, ... $n\lambda$, and these are called the waves of 2nd, 3rd, ... nth order. The greatest possible path difference for successive holes is a, so that n cannot be greater than a/λ. It will be seen that all the waves except that of zero order disappear if the spacing of the holes becomes irregular. It is only the regularity which makes it possible to find surfaces obeying the necessary conditions *for all the holes simultaneously*.

If the normal to the incident wave-fronts, instead of being

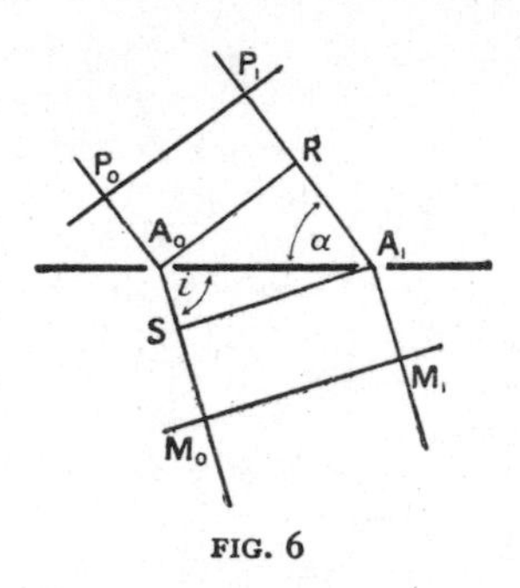

FIG. 6

perpendicular to the line of holes, makes an angle i with it, it will still be possible to construct the waves of the different orders. Suppose that the wave normal to the nth order wave makes an angle α with the line of holes. Let M_0M_1 ... (Fig. 6) be the trace of the incident wave, and P_0P_1 ... that of the nth order wave. The path difference for successive holes is evidently $A_1R - A_0S$, or $a(\cos\alpha - \cos i)$. For the nth order wave we must therefore have

$$a(\cos\alpha - \cos i) = n\lambda, \qquad (2)$$

and, for a given value of i, we may obtain the different diffracted wave-fronts by putting $n=0, 1, 2, 3, \ldots -1, -2, -3, \ldots$ in this equation. The wave of order n is a cone of semi-vertical angle $\pi/2-\alpha$, and the locus of the possible directions of the wave normal from any hole to it is a cone of semi-vertical angle α, both cones having the line of holes as axis.

We may apply these results immediately to the case of holes arranged, in a 2-dimensional pattern, at the intersections of two sets of parallel lines with spacings a and b, so that any hole is a member of one row with a spacing a and of a second with a spacing b. Let the wave normal to the incident wave make angles i_1 and i_2 with the directions of the rows of spacing a and b respectively. Now, as we have seen, the wavelets from the holes of any row a will agree in phase on a surface normal to a direction making an angle α with the direction of a, which is given by

$$a(\cos\alpha - \cos i_1) = n_1\lambda, \tag{3}$$

n_1 being a whole number, and, in the same way, all the wavelets from any row b will agree in phase on a surface whose normal makes an angle β with the direction of b, given by

$$b(\cos\beta - \cos i_2) = n_2\lambda. \tag{4}$$

Now, for a given pair of values of n_1 and n_2, there is one surface which satisfies these two conditions simultaneously, and that is the plane whose normal is defined by the angles α and β. Over this plane, the wavelets from all the holes in the pattern will agree in phase, and it is of course a diffracted wave-front. The possible diffracted waves from a 2-dimensional pattern are thus a series of diverging sets of plane waves, defined by the pairs of integers $(n_1 n_2)$, which may have any integral values, positive, negative, or zero, which enable conditions (3) and (4) to be satisfied simultaneously.

To include the diffraction of X rays by a crystal, we must now extend this reasoning to three dimensions. The crystal units, presumably groups of atoms, are arranged at the points of a space-lattice. As an X-ray wave sweeps through the crystal, each atom scatters a small fraction of the radiation, and the crystal units thus become the centres of scattered wavelets between which a definite phase relationship holds, owing to the regular spacing of the crystal lattice, and the fact that all the wavelets are derived from the same incident wave. To express this fact, we say that the scattered radiation is 'coherent'. We have therefore exactly the generalization to three dimensions of the cases considered above.

Let a, b, c, be the spacings of the lattice in the directions of the three axes, that is to say the primitive translations. Let the incident wave normal make angles i_1, i_2, i_3 with the axes of a, b, and c respectively. A diffracted wave-front, whose normal is defined by α, β, γ, the angles which it makes with the three axes, will be formed if

$$\left.\begin{aligned} a(\cos\alpha-\cos i_1)&=n_1\lambda \\ b(\cos\beta-\cos i_2)&=n_2\lambda \\ c(\cos\gamma-\cos i_3)&=n_3\lambda \end{aligned}\right\}, \qquad (5)$$

where n_1, n_2, n_3, are whole numbers.

Now these conditions are far more stringent than those for diffraction at a 2-dimensional grating. For a given direction of incidence, i_1, i_2 and i_3 are fixed. The first two conditions of (5) are satisfied by certain values of α and β, and these fix the corresponding values of γ, since two angles are sufficient to fix the direction of a line. For a given wave-length, therefore, when the first two conditions are satisfied, all the quantities in the third equation are already fixed except n_3, which must be a whole number. The three conditions cannot therefore in general be satisfied simultaneously except for $n_1=n_2=n_3=0$, which gives a wave in the same direction as the incident wave, the wave of zero order. We therefore conclude that if a beam of X rays of given wave-length is passed through a crystal at any arbitrary angle of incidence there will not in general be any diffracted beams. It will be necessary to use certain angles of incidence, or, for a given angle of incidence, to vary the wave-length, and so to add another degree of freedom to the equations (5), before a diffracted beam is produced.

BRAGG'S RULE

Another way of regarding this stringency of condition was pointed out by W. L. Bragg, in his first paper on the subject in 1912, and is of great importance. As we have seen in Chapter I, the points of a space-lattice may be thought of as lying in a set of similar, equally spaced, parallel planes. Suppose a parallel beam of X rays is incident in a direction making a glancing angle θ with the surfaces of the planes. Each plane must be thought of as reflecting a very small fraction of the incident beam, for the process of combining the wavelets scattered by the crystal units lying in one plane is precisely the Huyghens construction for the reflexion of plane waves at a plane surface. Any diffracted beam which does occur must therefore be in a direction corresponding to reflexion of the incident beam from a set of crystal planes. There will, however, be no diffracted beam unless the waves reflected from the different planes are exactly in phase. If

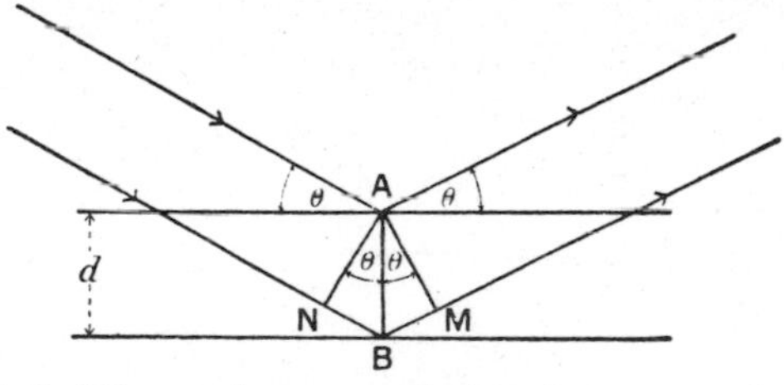

FIG. 7. Path difference between reflexions from successive planes
The path difference $=NB+BM=2d \sin \theta$

there is the smallest disagreement in phase between the beams reflected from successive planes, the regularity of the spacing of the planes, together with their huge number, will cause almost complete destructive interference. Now the path difference between reflected beams, derived from the same incident beam, and reflected at successive planes at a glancing angle θ, is easily seen from Fig. 7 to be $2d \sin \theta$, d being the spacing of the planes. Bragg's law may therefore be stated as follows. If a diffracted beam is produced when a beam of X rays passes through a crystal, it must be in such a direction that it may be considered as derived by reflexion of the incident beam from one of the sets of lattice planes, but such a reflexion can only occur if the condition

$$2d \sin \theta = n\lambda \qquad (6)$$

is satisfied, where θ is the glancing angle of incidence of the

X-ray beam on the planes in question and d is their spacing, n being an integer. This condition is of course mathematically equivalent to the conditions (5) given above: it provides, however, a very simple picture of the process of diffraction at a space-lattice, which is in practice nearly always thought of as reflexion at the lattice planes.

THE METHODS OF OBSERVING X-RAY DIFFRACTION SPECTRA

(1) **The Laue Method.** We have seen in the preceding section that if a beam of X rays of a given wave-length λ is passed in a given direction through a crystal, diffraction is not in general to be expected. We have also seen, however, that Friedrich and Knipping, on passing a beam of X rays through a slice of crystal, did in fact obtain diffraction. At first sight this result seems to contradict the theory, but a little consideration will show that this is not so. The directions of the incident beam and of the crystal planes are fixed, and this fixes the directions of the possible diffracted beams, for they are obtained by supposing the incident beam to be reflected in the crystal planes. For each set of planes, the angle θ of the Bragg condition is thus fixed, and the only variables are n and λ. Now n has to be an integer, and if λ were fixed also it would only be a matter of chance if there were any diffracted beams. But an X-ray bulb gives, in addition to the line spectrum characteristic of its target, a continuous X-ray spectrum over a considerable range of wave-lengths; λ is therefore variable, and it will in general be possible to find values to satisfy the reflexion condition. Each spot on the Laue photograph is produced by a different wave-length, and if it were possible to obtain an optical Laue pattern, the spots would be differently coloured. Examination of the Laue photograph shows that the spots do actually occur at the positions to be expected from the reflexion law. The spots are seen to lie on a series of ellipses which pass through the central spot (see Fig. 8). The spots on any one ellipse are produced by planes belonging to the same zone, that is to say, planes which are parallel to one common direction. Experimentally, the Laue method is comparatively easy. A narrow beam of X rays, limited by suitable lead slits,

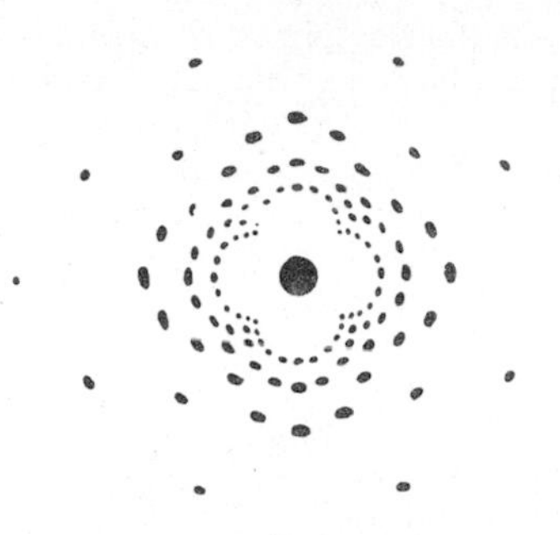

FIG. 8. The arrangement of the spots in a Laue photograph of a simple cubic crystal. X-ray beam perpendicular to a cube face

is allowed to pass through a slice of crystal, and then to fall normally on a photographic plate, wrapped in black paper and mounted in a convenient holder. The method has certain advantages, and, in skilful hands, has given valuable results, but the fact that the spectra are formed by different wave-lengths is a disadvantage and makes them difficult to interpret. We shall not consider the method in detail here.

(2) **The X-Ray Spectrometer.** The Laue method keeps the angle of incidence fixed, and alters the wave-length to satisfy the reflexion condition. Most other methods use X rays of a given wave-length, and alter the angle of incidence until the conditions are fulfilled. One of the earliest instruments using this method is the X-ray spectrometer, which was designed in 1913 by Sir William Bragg, and is founded very directly on the idea of reflexion at a set of crystal planes. Any face of a crystal is parallel to one of the sets of lattice planes. Suppose a beam of X rays of definite wave-length falls upon such a crystal face. There will in general be no reflected beam. If, however, the angle of incidence is adjusted to a value satisfying the reflexion condition, a reflected beam appears. The crystal, *C* in Fig. 9, is

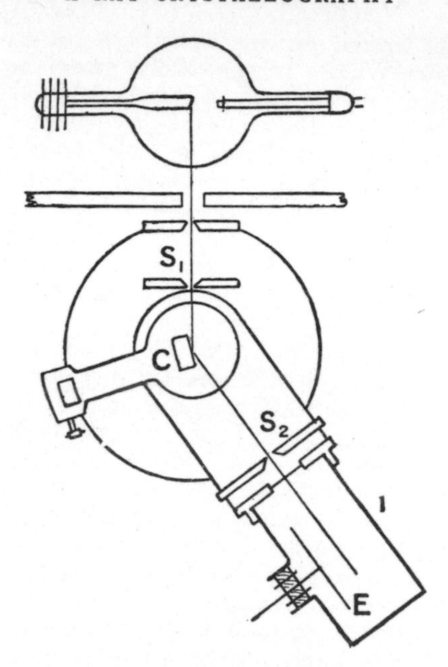

FIG. 9. The X-ray spectrometer

mounted on the table of a spectrometer, so that it can rotate about the axis of the instrument, the face from which reflexions are to be obtained being mounted so as to contain this axis. The collimator of the spectrometer is replaced by a system of slits, S_1, which allow a narrow beam of X rays to fall upon the crystal face. The telescope of the spectrometer is represented by an ionization chamber, *I*, which can rotate about the axis of the instrument, so as to receive any X-ray beam reflected from the crystal. The chamber has an aluminium foil window, and is provided with limiting slits S_2. It contains methyl bromide, or some other gas easily ionized by the X rays to be used. An insulated electrode *E* inside the chamber is connected to a sensitive electroscope, the outer coating of the chamber being kept at a potential of several hundred volts by a battery of small accumulators. When a beam of X rays enters the chamber, an ionization current is set up, which is detected by the electroscope.

An X-ray tube with a target of molybdenum or copper is generally used, which gives strongly the characteristic K radiation of the metal, superposed on a fainter continuous spectrum. The wave-lengths of the two chief lines, $K\alpha$ and $K\beta$ differ enough for the reflexion produced by $K\beta$ to be easily excluded by the slit of the chamber when that produced by $K\alpha$ is admitted, so that, virtually, the nearly monochromatic $K\alpha$ radiation is being used. The wave-lengths of the $K\alpha$ lines of Mo and Cu are respectively 0·710 and 1·540 Å, very suitable for giving diffraction effects with the lattice spacings that usually occur in crystals.[1]

In using the instrument to find X-ray spectra, the observer varies the angle of incidence, θ, of the X-ray beam on the crystal face by slowly rotating the crystal table. The chamber is rotated at the same time at twice the rate of the crystal, so that it is always in the correct position to receive a beam of rays reflected from the crystal face. Reflexion will occur only for the values of θ which satisfy the equation $2d \sin \theta = n\lambda$. The settings of the crystal at which reflexion occurs are very sharp, and the angles θ_1, θ_2, θ_3 ... corresponding to the different orders of reflexion can usually be determined to within a few minutes of arc, with ease.

The spectra may conveniently be denoted by the product of the Miller indices of the planes at which they are reflected and the order. Thus the first order from a (111) face would be called 111, the 3rd order 333, and so on. If the wave-length of the X rays is known, it is evident that the spacings of the planes can be determined from the spectrometer measurements. For example, with Mo $K\alpha$, 111 for the rock-salt crystal occurs at $\theta = 6^\circ\ 16'$, so that the spacing of the (111) planes is about 3·25 Å. If the spacings of a crystal have been determined, using a known wave-length, the instrument can be used as a spectrometer for X rays, and unknown

[1] Ångström unit = 1 Å = 10^{-8} cm.

wave-lengths may be determined. The first measurements of the wave-lengths of X rays were made by Sir William Bragg with this instrument.

The spectrometer method has the great advantage that a quantitative estimate of the intensity of the reflexions can be made, which, as we shall see later, is of the greatest importance in determining crystal structures.

In the earlier work with the X-ray spectrometer, large crystals of simple substances were generally used, and faces which did not occur naturally were ground or cut on the crystal in the proper directions; but many of the most interesting substances form minute crystals, often with no identifiable faces, and the ionization chamber is now generally replaced by a Geiger-Müller counter, connected to a counting-rate meter and scaling unit. Such a device is far more sensitive than the ionization chamber, and very small crystals, such as are suitable for the photographic methods to be described below may be used. In this way, it is possible, without undue labour, to compare with considerable accuracy the intensities of the spectra from all the planes lying in one zone. Adjustments to ensure that the zone axis of the crystal lies in the axis of rotation of the spectrometer are usually made photographically, in a manner that will be understood from the next section.

(3) **The Rotating-Crystal Method.** The methods most generally used in recording diffraction spectra from crystals are photographic, and some of these will now be considered. Suppose a beam of X rays to fall on a very small crystal, completely bathing it in radiation. The crystal does not completely absorb the radiation that falls on it, and reflexion can take place from the planes within it if the necessary conditions are fulfilled. If the crystal is set into slow rotation about a fixed axis, the sets of planes come successively into their reflecting positions, and the corresponding beams flash out for a moment, producing upon a photographic film set to receive them a pattern of spots, known as a rotation photograph. A large number of rotations will usually be necessary to produce a pattern of appreciable intensity. In the method now generally used, the film is

bent into the form of a cylinder, the axis of which is also the axis of rotation of the crystal.

Suppose the crystal to be mounted so that the c axis is parallel to the axis of rotation, to which the incident beam is perpendicular, and consider a spectrum formed in a direction making an angle ϕ with the axis. By equation (3), such a spectrum cannot be formed unless $c \cos \phi = n\lambda$, c being the lattice translation parallel to the c axis, and n a whole number (see Fig. 10). Any diffracted beams which do occur must therefore lie on the surfaces of a family of cones, whose vertices are at the crystal, and whose semi-vertical angles, ϕ, are obtained by putting $n=0, 1, 2, \ldots -1, -2, \ldots$ in the above relation. This family of cones will evidently intersect the cylindrical film in a series of circles (Fig. 11), lying in planes perpendicular to the axis of rotation, which become a series of parallel straight lines, known as layer lines, when the film is unrolled. Each layer line is denoted by the value of n to which it corresponds. The cone for $n=0$ is a plane perpendicular to the axis, and containing the direction of incidence, and the intersection of this with the film is called

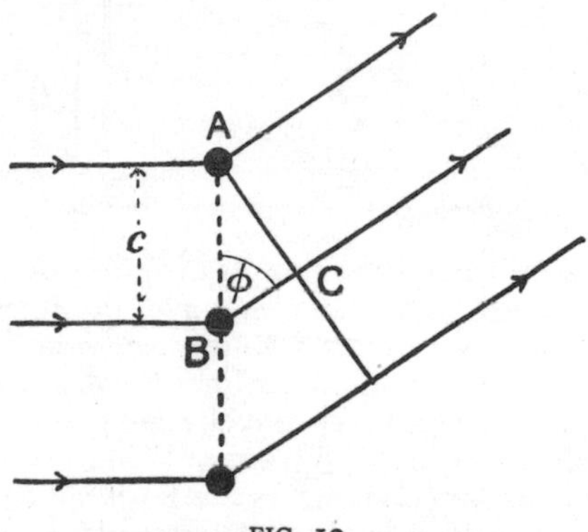

FIG. 10

The path difference between rays scattered from A and B is BC or $c \cos \phi$, and must be $n\lambda$ for a spectrum

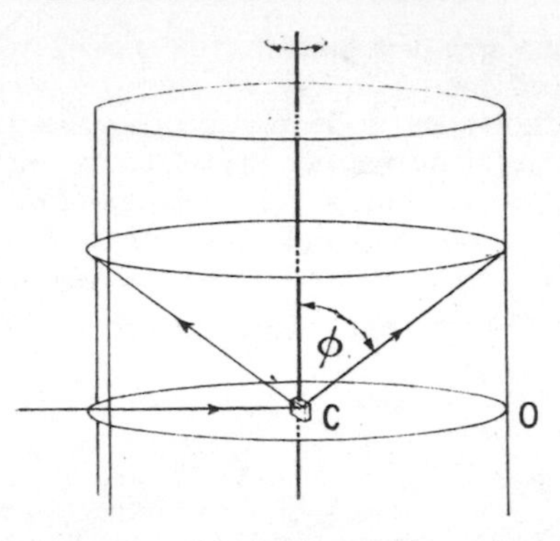

FIG. 11. The formation of layer lines with a cylindrical camera
The film is bent into the form of a cylinder

the equatorial, or zero layer line. If the index of a spectrum is denoted by *hkl*, and if, for example, the rotation takes place about the *c* axis, all spots on the zero layer line will have $l=0$, those on the first layer lines above and below the equatorial line $l=1$ or -1 respectively, and so on. Spots with the same values of *h* and *k*, but varying values of *l*, all lie on one of a series of curves known as row lines, which are transverse to the layer lines, and in the particular case in which *a* and *b* are perpendicular to the axis of rotation, intersect the zero layer line at right angles.

It is not possible to discuss in detail the methods used to determine the indices of the spectra from the position of the spots on the photograph. The important point for the present discussion is that, from the spacing of the layer lines, the lattice translation, that is to say, the distance in which the crystal pattern repeats itself in a direction parallel to the axis of rotation can at once be determined, for, if the distance of the film from the crystal is known, the distances of the layer lines from the equatorial line give at once the values of the angle ϕ, and so, λ being known, the value of *c*. If rotation photographs are taken separately about all three axes, the translations *a*, *b*, *c*, and hence the dimensions of the unit cell of the structure, are determined. The rotating-crystal method is thus very powerful: it gives the size of the unit cell, and a very large number of spectra, with a large range of indices, within the compass of three photographic films. With a complete rotation, however, so many spots are obtained upon the film as to produce confusion, and it is the usual practice to rotate the crystal backwards and forwards through an angular range of only about 15°, in order to limit the spots on any one photograph to those of certain possible indices.

A very powerful variation of the method, now much used, is due to Weissenberg. The crystal is rotated through 180° and back again, continuously, and at the same time the cylindrical camera containing the film moves at a constant speed backwards and forwards, parallel to the axis of rotation, the movements of camera and film being so synchronized that a given position of the camera corresponds accurately to a definite angular position of the crystal in its rotation. The co-ordinates of a spot on the film then give both the angle of reflexion and the position of the reflecting plane, and this allows the spot to be indexed without ambiguity. A metal cylinder, provided with an equatorial slit a few millimetres wide, is interposed between the crystal and the film in such a position that the spots of only one layer line can pass through it. The Weissenberg photograph records all the spots belonging to that layer line, spread out into a characteristic pattern on the single film, and with a little experience they can readily be indexed. The time of exposure necessary is much longer than that for an ordinary oscillation photograph. On the other hand, twelve or fifteen such photographs might sometimes be needed to give the same information.

(4) **The Powdered-Crystal Method.** In many truly crystalline solids, individual crystals large enough even for the rotating-crystal method never occur. Such substances can, however, be examined by a method devised independently by Debye and Scherrer in Germany, and by Hull in America, in which a monochromatic X-ray beam is allowed to fall on a small specimen of the substance ground to a fine powder. The orientation of the minute crystal fragments

being completely at random, a certain number of them will lie with any given set of lattice planes making exactly the correct angle with the incident beam for reflexion to occur. Let θ be one such glancing angle of reflexion. The only necessary condition is that the planes should make an angle θ with the incident beam. Any fragment, therefore, in which the normal to the plane in question makes an angle of $90°-\theta$ with the incident beam will be in a position to reflect, and since all orientations of the fragments are equally likely, the reflected rays will form a cone, whose axis is the direction of the incident beam, and whose semi-vertical angle is 2θ. For each set of planes, and for each order of spectrum, there is such a cone of diffracted rays: their intersections with a photographic plate set with its plane normal to the incident beam form a series of concentric circular haloes, from the radii of which the angles θ, and hence, the spacings of the planes can be deduced. It is generally necessary to obtain spectra for which the angle 2θ is more than a right angle, so that it is more usual to employ, instead of a plate, a cylindrical photographic film, nearly surrounding the crystal specimen. In one form of apparatus, the crystal powder is stuck, by means of gum, on a hair, which hangs vertically in the axis of a cylindrical camera, being stretched by means of a small weight. A strip of photographic film fits round the inner surface of the camera, covering nearly the whole circumference. A narrow X-ray beam, suitably limited by lead slits, falls on the powder, and afterwards passes out of the camera through a hole cut in the film, in order to minimize the fogging produced by the scattering of the direct beam.

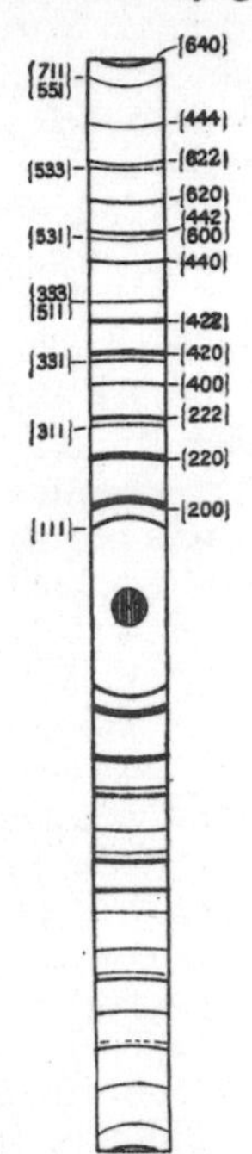

FIG. 12. Arrangement of lines in a powder photograph of NaCl Radiation CuKa, $\lambda=1{\cdot}54$ Å

The intersections with the film of the cones of rays diffracted from the powder produce a series of lines, each of which corresponds to a definite value of the glancing angle θ, and so, to a given spacing. A diagram of a typical powder photograph is shown in Fig. 12. In Fig. 13, P is the powder, O is the point where the direct beam would have struck the film, and A the point on the film, in a plane at right angles to the axis of the camera, and containing the incident beam, at which a spectrum with glancing angle θ is formed. If l is the distance from O to A, measured on the film, and R is the radius of the camera, we have, from the figure, $\theta = l/2R$, so

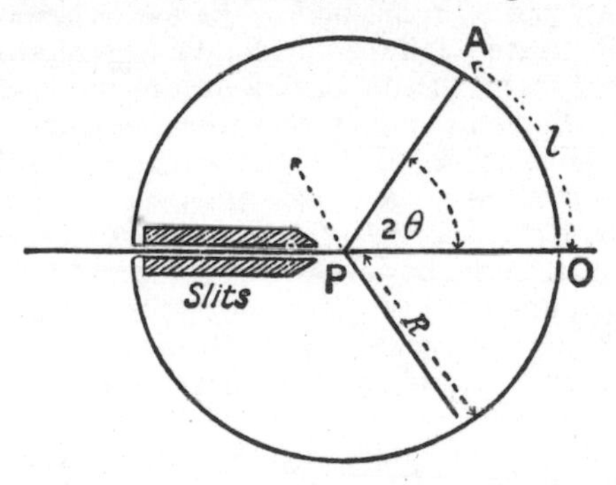

FIG. 13. The formation of a powder photograph

that by measuring l for the lines on the film the values of θ can be determined. It is possible to determine spacings very accurately indeed if only lines that have been deflected through nearly 180° are used, since the variation of θ with spacing is then a maximum, and the measured value of the angle depends very little on small displacements of the crystal from the exact axis of rotation.

The powder photograph method is of great use in investigating the structures of simple crystals, particularly of those belonging to the cubic system for which the spacings a, b, c, of the unit cell are all equal. For such crystals there are certain definite relationships between the angles at which spectra can occur, which makes the identification of the lines easy. Moreover, the spacings of all the planes parallel to faces of the same form $\{hkl\}$ are equal, and therefore produce spectra at the same angle. For the most general case, in which h, k, and l are all different, there are 48 faces in the form and 24 sets of planes all having the same spacing, and these all co-operate to produce one line on the film. Suppose now all the three axes are of different length, while still remaining at right angles to one another. The same general form $\{hkl\}$ now corresponds to six different spacings, and hence, to six different lines on the film. For crystals in which the axes are not at right angles, the multiplication of the lines is still greater, and the powder photograph becomes so complicated that it has hitherto been scarcely practicable to identify the lines, although recent work suggests that it may yet be possible to do so. For the actual determination of structures, therefore, the powder method has been of real value only for cubic, tetragonal, and hexagonal crystals. These types include, however, most of the metals and alloys, and a large number of simple binary compounds, the structures of which, owing to their habit of never crystallizing in large crystals, could not have been determined but for the powder method.

The powder photograph of a substance is characteristic of it, and can be used to identify it even if the crystal structure cannot be worked out.

THE DETERMINATION OF THE STANDARD CRYSTAL SPACING

By using one of the methods described in the last section, it is possible to determine the unit cell of a crystal structure, that is to say the shape and dimensions of the units of pattern which, stacked together in countless millions, make up the crystal. So far as we have gone at present, it appears to be possible to determine the dimensions of the unit cell only in terms of the wave-length of the radiation used in the investigation. This is of course true, so long as we confine ourselves solely to what may be learnt from diffraction by the crystal lattice: nevertheless, for some very simple crystals, it is possible to determine the actual dimensions of the unit and so, the wave-length of the X rays. The first determinations of this kind were made in 1913 by Sir William Bragg, using rock-salt and potassium chloride, in which the arrangement of the atoms had just been determined by W. L. Bragg. Each crystal has an exactly similar structure of the type

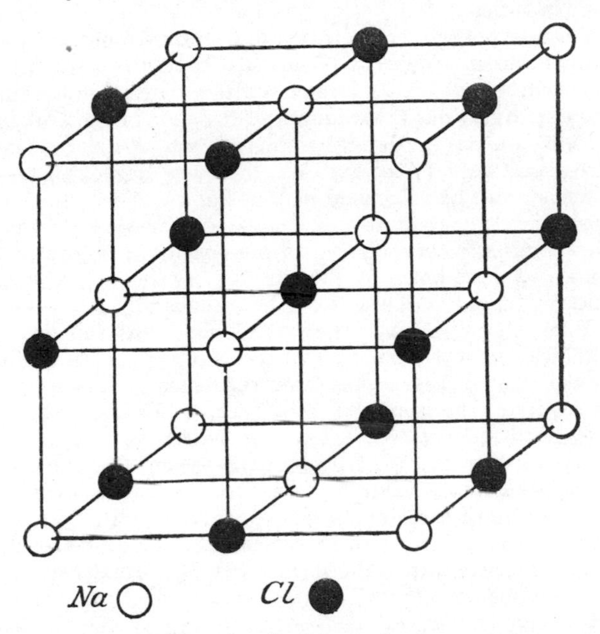

FIG. 14. The unit cell of the rock-salt structure

shown in Fig. 14, and we shall consider the case of rock-salt. The crystals are cubic, each atom being a member of three equally spaced rows at right angles to one another, the atoms of Na and Cl always occurring alternately. Each Na atom has therefore 6 Cl atoms, and each Cl atom 6 Na atoms, as neighbours. The unit of structure which we obtain by starting, for example, with any Na atom, going along each axis in turn to the next Na atom, and completing the cube so defined, will be found to consist of a cube with a Na atom at each corner, and one in the middle of each face. The Na atoms, in other words, lie on a face-centred cubic lattice. So of course do the Cl atoms, their lattice being displaced half the edge of the unit cell along each axis with respect to the Na lattice.

Now such a unit cell contains four of each kind of atom,[1] and so four molecules of NaCl. Let M be the actual mass of a molecule of NaCl: the mass of the material in the unit cell is $4M$ gm. But if the length of the edge of the unit cell is a cm., and ρ is the density of the rock-salt crystal, the mass of the unit cube is ρa^3 gm. We therefore have $a^3=4M/\rho$, whence a can be calculated if M is known. Now, from the spectrometer measurements, the glancing angle θ at which the spectrum corresponding to the spacing a is formed is known, and we have, by Bragg's rule, $2a \sin \theta=\lambda$, whence, since we already know a, λ can be calculated.

The determination of the wave-length thus depends on a knowledge of M, the mass of the NaCl molecule, and so on the mass of the hydrogen atom, which in its turn, for its accurate determination, requires a knowledge of e, the charge on an electron. If we use Millikan's value of e, $4{\cdot}774 \cdot 10^{-10}$ e.s.u., the length of the side of the unit cube of rock-salt comes out to be $5{\cdot}628 \cdot 10^{-8}$ cm. at the ordinary temperature of the laboratory. All wave-length determinations based on diffraction by crystal lattices depend on this standard spacing, or on the corresponding one deduced from observations on calcite. The relative values of X-ray wave-lengths are known with considerable accuracy; the absolute values, which are based on one of the standard lattice spacings, depend on e, and would all be changed by a change in the accepted value of this constant.

Compton and Doan, using the fact that X rays are totally reflected at very small glancing angles from a smooth surface, and that the path differences for the successive elements

[1] Each atom at a cell corner is shared by eight cells, and so contributes $\frac{1}{8}$ atom to the unit, and each atom in a cell face is shared by two cells and so contributes $\frac{1}{2}$ an atom.

of a reflexion grating become extremely small for glancing angles of a few minutes, were able to obtain optical diffraction of X rays from a ruled grating, and so to determine the wave-length directly, in terms of the measured grating space. The value obtained was in good agreement with that obtained from crystal measurements, and Compton's experiment is of the greatest importance on account of the check it gives of the general accuracy in principle of the methods used to obtain the true dimensions of crystal structures. It is clear, however, that if the directly measured wave-length is taken as the primary constant, a value of the electronic charge can be obtained from measurements of the diffraction of X rays by crystals. Accurate work on these lines by Bearden and others, and also work on the diffraction of electrons, has in fact led to a revision of Millikan's value of e, which is now taken as $4{\cdot}803 \times 10^{-10}$ e.s.u. The standard tables of X-ray wave-lengths have not, however, been changed. Their relative accuracy is probably of the order of 0·001 per cent, but the values are not expressed in Ångström units (10^{-8} cm.) but in so-called kX units. To convert these into Ångström units if the revised value of e is correct it is necessary to multiply by a factor of 1·0020.

In determining an unknown structure, the wave-length is taken as known, and the actual size of the unit cell is determined from the spacings of the layer lines on rotation photographs, or otherwise. Then, from the density of the crystal, and its chemical composition, the number of molecules in the unit cell is calculated. This is only the first step: a complete determination of the structure involves finding the positions occupied by the individual atoms in the unit cell; but before considering how this may be done it will be necessary to return for a time to the purely geometrical aspect of the subject, and in continuation of the matters discussed in Chapter I, to take up the study of crystal symmetry.

CHAPTER III

THE SYMMETRY OF CRYSTALS AND ITS DETERMINATION BY MEANS OF X RAYS

EXTERNAL SYMMETRY

STUDY of the external forms of crystals reveals the fact that most of them possess geometrical symmetry. A geometrical figure is said to possess symmetry if, by performing on it some geometrical operation, such as rotation about an axis, or reflexion across a plane, it can be brought into self-coincidence. For example, a square can be brought into self-coincidence by rotating it through a right angle about an axis perpendicular to its plane and passing through its centre, or by reflecting it across a plane passing through its centre and perpendicular to its sides, and in a number of other ways. In studying the symmetry of crystals, we consider not the actual form of any real crystal, which will depend on the accidents of growth, but the radiating bundle of normals to its faces from some internal fixed point, or the points where these normals cut a sphere whose centre is their origin, which, as we have seen in Chapter I, are the true representations of the geometrical form of the crystal.

It is found as a matter of observation that, so far as the external forms of crystals are concerned, the following elements of symmetry may occur:

(*a*) **2-fold, 3-fold, 4-fold or 6-fold (but not 5-fold) rotation-axes of symmetry.** A figure is said to possess an *n*-fold rotation axis of symmetry if it is brought into self-coincidence by a rotation of $2\pi/n$ about that axis. The symmetry axis of the square mentioned above is a 4-fold axis. These axes are also called digonal, trigonal, tetragonal and hexagonal axes.

(*b*) **Centres of Symmetry.** If a figure has a centre of

symmetry, O, then to every point A of the figure there corresponds a point A' such that AOA' is a straight line, and $OA = OA'$.

(*c*) **Reflexion Planes of Symmetry.** A figure has a reflexion plane of symmetry if by reflexion in that plane, as in a mirror, but in both directions, the figure is brought into self-coincidence.

(*d*) **4-fold and 6-fold Alternating Axes, or Rotation-Reflexion Axes.** The operation of an n-fold alternating axis consists of a rotation through $2\pi/n$ about the axis, followed by a reflexion across a plane at right angles to the axis. n must evidently be even, and a 2-fold alternating axis is equivalent to a centre of symmetry, so that $n=4$ and $n=6$ are the only possibilities. A rhomb of calcite has, for example, a 6-fold alternating axis.

The geometrical forms of crystals may be classified according to their possession of one or more of the symmetry elements enumerated above. Since we are dealing with the symmetry of a set of normals radiating from a point, it follows that any symmetry planes or axes concerned must go through this point. We have therefore a perfectly definite geometrical problem. What combinations of the above symmetry elements are possible, subject to the conditions that all of them pass through a single point? A group of symmetry elements of this kind is known as a **Point Group.** It is found that 32 such groups are possible, so that there should be 32 possible classes of crystal, arranged according to the symmetry of their external forms. These 32 classes do in fact include all the known types of crystal symmetry, and, with a few doubtful exceptions, examples of every class are known.

CRYSTAL SYSTEMS

The crystal classes may be divided into seven main **Systems,** each characterized by the possession of a certain minimum of symmetry elements, and referable to certain characteristic axes. The systems are:

(1) **Triclinic,** possessing no symmetry at all, or, at the most, a symmetry centre. In the first case opposite faces will

have different properties, in the second, the same properties. Referable to 3 unequal axes, not at right angles.

(2) **Monoclinic,** possessing a single 2-fold axis, or a single reflexion plane. Referable to 3 unequal axes, one at right angles to the other two.

(3) **Orthorhombic,** having two symmetry planes at right angles, or three 2-fold axes at right angles to one another. The existence of two such axes demands the existence of a third. Referable to 3 unequal axes at right angles.

(4) **Trigonal,** having a single 3-fold axis. Referable to 3 equal axes equally inclined to the 3-fold axis.

(5) **Tetragonal,** having a single 4-fold axis, simple or alternating. Referable to 3 axes at right angles, two of them equal.

(6) **Hexagonal,** having a single 6-fold axis, simple or alternating. Referable to 2 equal axes inclined at 120° and a third, unequal axis at right angles to them.

(7) **Cubic or Regular,** having four 3-fold axes, corresponding in direction to the diagonals of a cube. Referable to 3 equal axes at right angles to one another.

The symmetry elements given above are in each case the minimum required to place the crystal in the system in question; they are not, however, in general incompatible with the existence of other symmetry elements at the same time, and in fact the existence of two symmetry elements in general conditions the existence of others. For example, two 2-fold axes at right angles demand a third at right angles to both (Fig. 15*b*). Adding a symmetry centre to these also adds three reflexion planes at right angles to one another, and the group has now the highest symmetry of the orthorhombic system (Fig. 15*c*). Starting in this way with the lowest symmetry requirements of each system, we may add one by one the compatible symmetry elements, until the highest possible symmetry of the system has been reached. This procedure gives in all 32 point-groups of symmetry elements, corresponding to the 32 crystal classes. The three point-groups of the orthorhombic system are shown in Fig. 15.

If a crystal belongs to a particular class, it must possess, corresponding to any one face, all the other faces which can

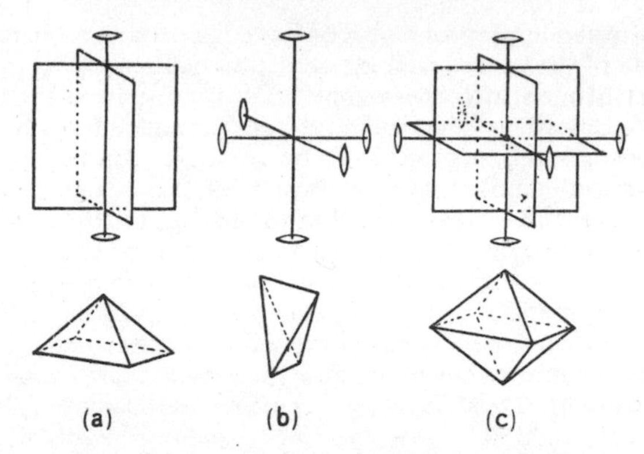

FIG. 15. The three point-groups of the orthorhombic system with their corresponding geometrical forms

(*a*) Di-digonal polar (Miers). Two reflexion planes at right angles and a 2-fold axis
(*b*) Digonal holoaxial. Three 2-fold axes at right angles
(*c*) Di-digonal equatorial. Three 2-fold axes, three reflexion planes and a centre of symmetry

be derived from the first by the symmetry operations belonging to the class. The faces will not of course as a rule be equally well developed on any particular crystal. The class having the highest possible symmetry for a system is called the **holohedral** class of that system. Classes having less than the full symmetry are called **hemihedral** or **tetartohedral** (having half or a quarter of the complete set of faces). It is quite usual, however, to refer to any class having less than the full symmetry of its system as hemihedral. A regular tetrahedron, for example, has hemihedral cubic symmetry. It has the four 3-fold axes characteristic of that system, but it has only six of the nine possible reflexion planes, the three 4-fold axes have become 4-fold alternating axes, and the six 2-fold axes, and the symmetry centre have vanished.

THE SYMMETRY OF SPACE-LATTICES

We must now consider how far the observed symmetry properties of crystals are in harmony with the idea of the crystal as founded on a space-lattice. In studying the symmetry of space-lattices, it is essential to realize that we are no longer dealing with axes and planes of symmetry all of which pass through a single point. If an element of symmetry passes through any point of one cell of an infinite lattice, a precisely similar element must pass through the corresponding points of every cell of the lattice, for the cells are all exactly similar, and not to be distinguished from each other in any way. Each one of these symmetry elements must, moreover, bring the whole lattice, including all the other symmetry elements, into self-coincidence, and only those symmetry elements, and their combinations, which are consistent with these requirements are possible. A little consideration will show that this explains the absence of 5-fold axes, for it is not possible to arrange such axes in this way.

Bravais showed, many years ago, that there are 14 possible types of space-lattice, one triclinic, two monoclinic, four orthorhombic, one rhombohedral, one hexagonal, two tetragonal and three cubic. The classification of the lattices refers to their symmetry as a whole, and not to that of their true unit cells. This will be clearer from the consideration of an example, and we shall take the case of the three cubic lattices. The simplest cubic lattice is that in which the lattice points lie at the corners of cubes. The three primitive translations are all equal, and at right angles, and this is the true cubic space-lattice. The other cubic lattices are the face-centred cube, which we have already met with in the case of NaCl, having a point at each corner of a cube and one in the middle of each face; and the body-centred cube, having a point at each cube corner and one at the cube centre. These lattices are classed as cubic because they have full cubic symmetry; they are not, however, cubic space-lattices in the sense that their primitive translations are at right angles. If, in the face-centred lattice shown in Fig. 16, for example, we start from any point of the lattice and take three axes at right angles, we can never include more than the points at the cube corners. Those at the face centres, or three-quarters of the total number of points, are left out. The face-centred

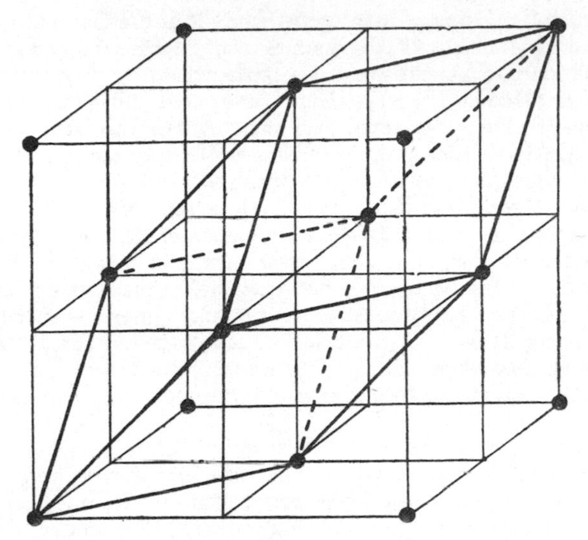

FIG. 16. The true unit cell of the face-centred cubic lattice

cube is, nevertheless, a true space-lattice, although not a cubic one. If we start at a cube corner and draw lines to the three nearest face centres of the same cube, we may take these lines as the primitive translations of a rhombohedral lattice which will include all the points. Its unit cell, which is outlined in Fig. 16, has one-quarter of the volume of the cube. The face-centred lattice is thus a special case of a rhombohedral, or hexagonal, lattice, which happens to possess cubic symmetry; and in a similar way it can be shown that the same is true of the body-centred lattice. Similar considerations apply to lattices belonging to the other systems.

Each of the 14 types of space-lattice has the fullest possible, or holohedral, symmetry of its system, and thus, so far as space-lattice symmetry alone is concerned, there are only seven types of symmetry. Now we have seen that crystals of 32 classes of external symmetry are known, and it follows, therefore, that something other than the symmetry of the fundamental space-lattice must come in in determining the actual symmetry of a crystal. Bravais recognized this, and pointed out that the symmetry of the whole structure would be reduced if the crystal-unit associated with the lattice point had a symmetry lower than that of the lattice as a whole. In deducing the possible symmetry of space-lattices, the assumption is made that the lattice points are mathematical points, and are completely symmetrical: if we replace the mathematical point by a geometrical figure, or by a collection of points, the symmetry of the whole lattice cannot be higher than that of the figure, or group of points. In this way Bravais explained the phenomenon of hemihedrism. It was only necessary to ascribe to the lattice units the symmetries of the various crystal classes to account for all the observed types of crystal symmetry.

THE SPACE-GROUP

For the X-ray crystallographer, the Bravais unit becomes a group of atoms in the unit cell, and if, for the time being, we can treat each atom as having spherical symmetry, or as a point, the geometrical problem which arises may be stated as follows. What types of symmetry are possible for a collection of exactly similar groups of points, each group being associated with one of the points of a Bravais lattice, and derived from any other group by the translations of the lattice? Fortunately for the rapid development of the subject, the answer to this purely geometrical question was already known at the time when the diffraction of X rays was discovered, owing mainly to the work of Sohncke, Fedorow, Schoenflies and Barlow.

The problem is that of combining symmetry elements into a space pattern. We have seen that, if a symmetry element passes through any point in one lattice cell, a similar element must pass through the corresponding point in every other cell. The existence of the symmetry elements in general demands the existence of others, and other additional symmetry elements may be combined with those already present, again in the same way in each unit cell; but any possible symmetry element must always be such as to bring, by its operation, the whole group of symmetry elements into self-coincidence. The assumption is of course made all through that the groups are of infinite extent. Each such possible group of symmetry elements is called a **Space-Group,** and their total number is found to be 230. It is very important to realize that a space-group is a group, or scaffolding, of symmetry elements, and not a group of points. If a geometrical point is placed anywhere in such a group, it is multiplied by the action of the symmetry elements into a collection of points associated with a lattice cell, and, by

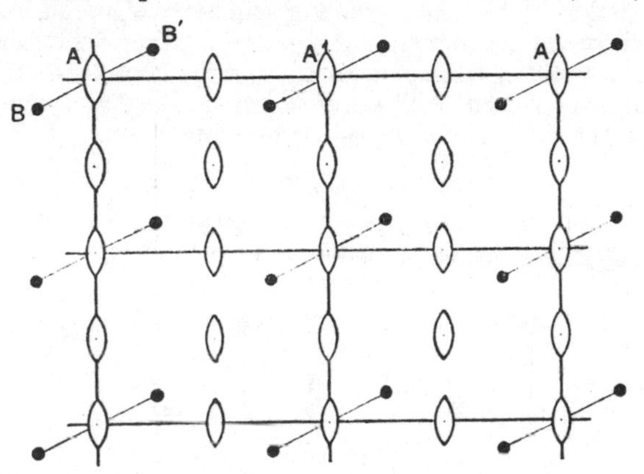

FIG. 17. Arrangement of 2-fold rotation axes, denoted by ⨀, perpendicular to a rectangular network

the translations of the lattice, into a similar collection of points associated with each cell, that is to say, into a pattern in space. An infinite number of different patterns could be produced according to the exact position of the original point, but all would have the same symmetry elements, and would belong to the same space-group.

We shall consider a 2-dimensional example. Suppose that Fig. 17 represents part of an infinite rectangular network, at each point A of which is a 2-fold rotation axis, perpendicular to the plane of the net. Remembering that the pattern is supposed to extend indefinitely in all directions in the plane, we see that each of the 2-fold axes by its action, a rotation through 180°, brings the whole set of axes into self-coincidence. If a point *B* is placed near one of the axes, it is turned by the axis into *B′*, and the translations of the lattice then produce exactly similar pairs of points about each *A* axis. It will now be seen from the figure that there are, in addition to the *A* axes, other sets of 2-fold axes, in the middle of each rectangle of the net, and at the mid-point of each side, half-way between the *A* axes. The existence of the *A* axes necessitates the existence of these other axes, and the action of the whole group of symmetry elements on the single point *B* produces the pattern. Other independent points could of course be put in, and the complexity of the pattern increased. Any set of points derived by symmetry from the same point are said to be **equivalent.**

GLIDE PLANES AND SCREW AXES

Certain symmetry elements are possible in an extended group which are not possible in a point group. These are

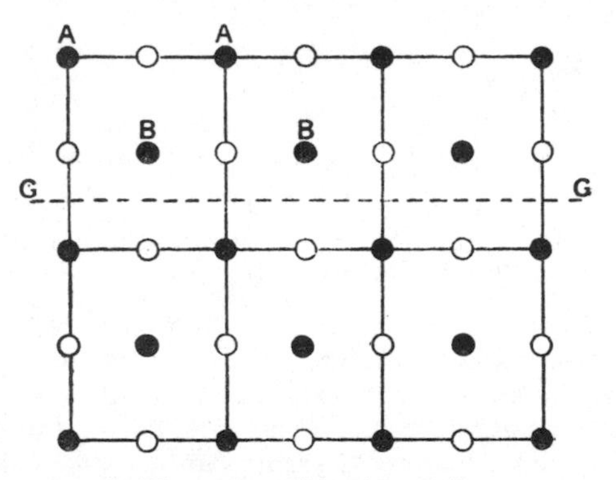

FIG. 18. Illustrating glide planes of symmetry

glide planes and screw axes. The nature of a glide plane may be understood from Fig. 18. The black circles *B* lie at the midpoints of the rectangles formed by the black circles *A*, all the circles *A* and *B* being alike. Let *GG′* be the trace of a plane, perpendicular to the plane of the paper, and half-way between the lines of circles A and B. By reflexion across this plane, the black circles are brought to the positions shown by the white circles in the diagram, and if these are given a translation, parallel to the plane of reflexion, of one-half the spacing AA, they coincide again with the original A and B circles. The whole figure is, in effect, brought into coincidence by a reflexion across GG' and a translation of half the lattice spacing parallel to the plane of reflexion. If now we imagine the figure extended to three dimensions, so that a set of points similar to A lie at equal intervals exactly below them, the B points being supposed to lie in planes half-way between the A planes, the figure can again be brought into self-coincidence by a reflexion across GG' and a glide, parallel to the plane, of half the A spacing in the plane of the paper plus half the A spacing in a direction perpendicular to the plane of the paper. These examples illustrate the two types of glide plane.

An n-fold screw axis produces a rotation of $2\pi/n$ about the axis and a translation parallel to the axis whose amount depends on n. If, in Fig. 18, we now take GG' as an axis, instead of as a trace of a plane, we see that a rotation of 180° about GG', together with a translation of $\frac{1}{2}AA$ parallel to the axis, brings the figure into self-coincidence. The translation, for a 2-fold screw axis, is always half the spacing of the lattice in the direction of the axis; for a 3-fold axis it is $\frac{1}{3}$, and, in the simplest cases, for the 4-fold and 6-fold axes, $\frac{1}{4}$ and $\frac{1}{6}$ of the spacing respectively. In all these cases except that of the 2-fold axis, the equivalent points are arranged spirally about the axes, and we have to distinguish between right- and left-handed rotations. For a 4-fold axis a translation of $\frac{1}{2}$ is also possible, this axis giving an arrangement of equivalent points which has also a 2-fold rotation axis. A 6-fold screw axis with a translation of $\frac{1}{3}$ may be either right- or left-handed, and the resulting arrangements of points have at the same time a 2-fold rotation axis and a 3-fold screw axis, while a translation of $\frac{1}{2}$ gives a set of points having a 3-fold rotation axis and a 2-fold screw axis.

The addition of these new kinds of symmetry element

and the fact that, in a space-group, the planes and axes do not all pass through one point, greatly increases the number of combinations of symmetry elements which are possible, and we need not be surprised that the number of groups has increased from 32, for the external form alone, to 230 when the inner structure is taken into account. If we take as an example the class of the orthorhombic system having three 2-fold axes, we shall find that, instead of the one possibility

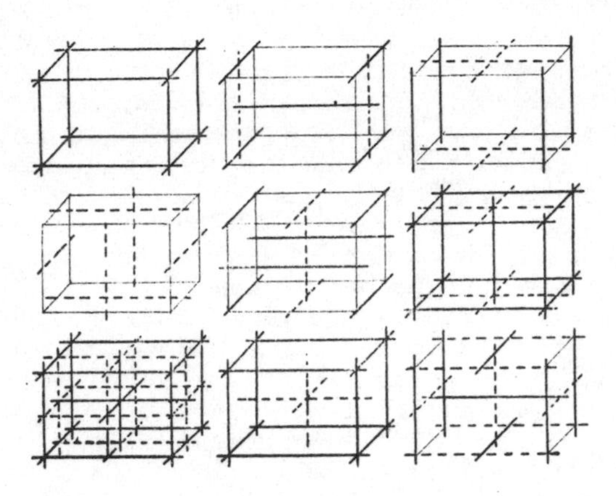

FIG. 19. The nine space-groups of the orthorhombic holoaxial class (three 2-fold axes at right angles, cf. Fig. 15*b*)

Each parallelepiped is ⅛ of the corresponding unit cell. Rotation axes denoted by thick continuous lines, screw axes by dotted lines

for the point group, there are nine ways, which are illustrated in Fig. 19, of combining three such axes, including of course screw axes. These all correspond to one crystal class, or, in other words, to one type of external symmetry. If we add a centre of symmetry to the axes, so as to produce the holohedral class of the system, we find that there are 28 possible combinations of axes and symmetry centres, or 28 holohedral orthorhombic space-groups. There are, in all, 60 space-groups in the orthorhombic system, corresponding to only three point groups, or classes of external symmetry.

THE COMPOUND SPACE-LATTICE

Before we proceed to discuss the determination of the space-lattice and the space-group, a little further geometrical preparation is necessary. We suppose the crystal to consist of exactly similar groups of atoms, indistinguishable either in themselves or in their surroundings, and therefore associated with the points of a space-lattice. Now each atom in the unit of structure must lie on its own space-lattice, which is equal and parallel to the lattice upon which the whole structure is based; for each atom in a given unit is to be derived from the corresponding atom in any other unit simply by the translations of this lattice. We have therefore the following important result. **A crystal structure having *N* atoms in the unit cell may be regarded as consisting of *N* equal and parallel inter-penetrating space-lattices, one for each atom of the unit.** Now we have seen that the atoms of any one space-lattice may be considered as lying on sets of equally spaced and identical planes. To each of the lattices of which, as we have just seen, we may suppose a structure to be built up there will correspond sets of planes. The planes characterized by given indices (hkl) will be parallel for all the lattices, but they will not in general coincide, and, instead of a single set of exactly equal planes repeating at a definite interval d, there will be identical groups of N planes repeating in the same interval. Since all the lattices are alike, each plane of a group will have the same number of atoms per unit area, the atoms on any one plane being all of one kind. It may happen that some of the planes of the group will coincide, but, in general, there will be one for each atom of the unit. The matters discussed in this paragraph are illustrated in two dimensions in Fig. 20, in which the space-lattices are represented by net-planes and the lattice planes by rows of points.

THE REFLEXION OF X RAYS BY A COMPOUND LATTICE

We must now consider the reflexion of X rays from a compound lattice such as that discussed in the last section, in which the single planes of the simple lattice are replaced

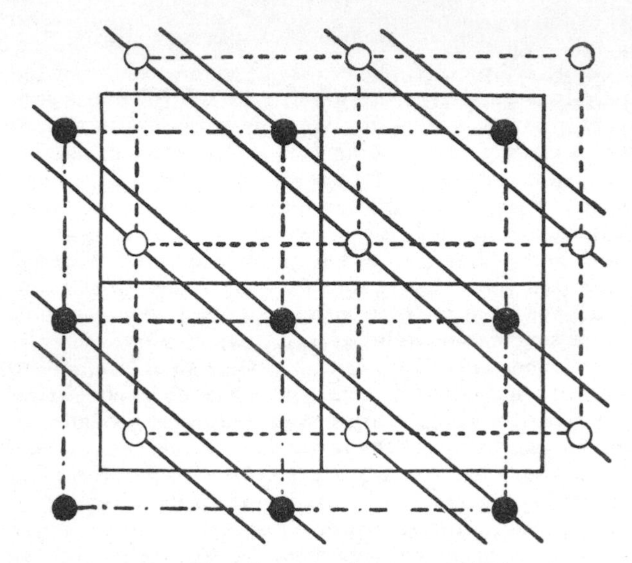

FIG. 20. Two-dimensional compound lattice

Each kind of point lies on its own 2-dimensional lattice. The rows of points occur in pairs, one row for each kind of point

by groups of planes. The angles at which the spectra are formed are just the same as for the simple lattice, since they depend only on the interval in which the pattern repeats itself, which may conveniently be termed the **identity period** for the set of planes. If, at any angle, the reflexions from the planes of atoms of one kind, A say, in successive groups of planes are in phase with one another, so are those from the planes of atoms of another kind, B, and so on for all the N kinds of plane. The reflexions from the different planes belonging to the *same* group will not, however, in general be in phase, so that the total amplitude reflected from the group will be less than it would have been had all the planes been coincident.

Suppose, for example, that the group consists of two planes only, one of kind A, the other of kind B. Let d be the spacing between successive planes of the same kind, or the identity period of the lattice in the direction concerned, and let x be the distance between the A and B planes of the same group. For a first order reflexion, the phase difference corresponding to a distance d is 2π, for there is a path difference of λ between the beams reflected from successive planes of the same kind. The phase difference between the beams reflected from a plane A and a plane B at a distance x apart is therefore $2\pi x/d$ for the first order, and $2\pi mx/d$ for the mth order. If the B planes are exactly half-way between the A planes, so that $x=d/2$, the phase difference for the mth order becomes $m\pi$. In this case, for the spectra of even order, the reflexions from the planes A and B are exactly in phase, while, for the spectra of odd order, they are exactly out of phase. If the A and B planes had been coincident, so that the reflexions from them were in phase for all orders of spectra, the latter, as we shall see later, would have fallen away regularly in intensity as the order increased. We may call such a set of spectra a **normal** series. With the B planes half-way between the A planes, we see that the spectra will be alternately weaker than and equal to those of the normal series. This case is realized by the (111) planes of NaCl, which consist of alternate sheets of Na and Cl atoms, and the spectra from these planes do in fact show this alternation in intensity. If the atoms A and B had been of the same kind, the odd orders of spectra would have been entirely absent, for in this case planes of the same kind would repeat at intervals $d/2$, instead of d, and the first order from planes with a spacing $d/2$ will of course occur at the same angle as the second order from planes with spacing d.

We see, then, that the interval in which the pattern repeats itself, or the identity period of the structure, determines the angles at which the spectra occur, but that the distribution of the atoms in the unit cell, which determines the spacing of the planes of the individual groups, controls the intensities of the spectra. It is by studying the intensities, therefore, that we may hope to determine the actual arrangement of the atoms.

CALCULATION OF THE PHASE DIFFERENCES

We shall now show how to calculate the phase differences between the reflexions from the planes of the different constituent lattices. The first step is to calculate the spacing of the planes (hkl) of a simple lattice with translations a, b, c.

Let one of the lattice points be taken as the origin of co-ordinates, referred to axes, x, y, z which lie in the direction of the lattice translations a, b, c, respectively. The perpendicular distance from a point whose co-ordinates referred to these axes are (x, y, z) to a plane through the origin, the normal to which has direction cosines λ, μ, ν, is $\lambda x+\mu y+\nu z$, and, as we have seen in Chapter I, if this plane is one of the set (hkl), λ, μ, and ν are proportional to h/a, k/b, and l/c respectively. Let us denote them by Dh/a, Dk/b, and Dl/c, so that the perpendicular distance from (x, y, z) to the plane is $D(hx/a+ky/b+lz/c)$.

The general co-ordinates of a lattice point are (ma, nb, pc), m, n, and p being integers, positive, negative or zero. The perpendicular distance from this point to the plane through the origin is therefore $D(mh+nk+pl)$. One plane of the set (hkl) passes through each lattice point, and the perpendicular distance we have calculated is that between this plane and the corresponding plane through the origin. The *spacing*, or identity period, of the (hkl) planes is the distance between successive planes of the set, and is therefore the least value of $D(mh+nk+pl)$, exclusive of zero. Since h, k, l, m, n, p are all integers, and m, n, p may have any values, positive or negative, including zero, the smallest value of $(mh+nk+pl)$ not zero is evidently unity. Thus D is the spacing of the (hkl) planes.

If the lattice is orthorhombic, the sum of the squares of the direction cosines of the plane must be unity, and this gives at once for D the value $1/\sqrt{(h^2/a^2+k^2/b^2+l^2/c^2)}$, which becomes $a/\sqrt{(h^2+k^2+l^2)}$ for a simple cubic lattice. If the lattice is not orthogonal the expression is more complicated, and involves the angles between the crystal axes.

Suppose, now, that the unit of structure consists of a group of N atoms, A, B, C, ..., which we shall suppose associated with each point of the lattice considered in the last paragraph. As before, we take axes parallel to the lattice translations, and choose a convenient origin, which may or may not contain an atom. Let (x, y, z) be the co-ordinates of some atom in the unit. A plane (hkl) passes through this atom, and through the corresponding atoms in the other units, and this is one of the N planes of the composite (hkl) group corresponding to the complex unit of structure. A beam of X rays is supposed reflected in turn from the plane (hkl) passing through the point (x, y, z) and from the parallel plane through the origin. Let us calculate the phase difference, ϕ, between the two reflected wave-trains when both contribute to the mth order spectrum from the (hkl) planes of the compound lattice. The distance between the two planes is the perpendicular distance from the point (x, y, z) on to the plane (hkl) through the origin, which, as we have already seen, is $D(hx/a+ky/b+lz/c)$. Since the spacing D corresponds to a phase difference of $2m\pi$ in the mth order spectrum, the phase difference, ϕ, between the wave-trains reflected from the plane through the point (x, y, z) and that through the origin is given by

$$\begin{aligned}\phi &= 2\pi m(hx/a+ky/b+lz/c)\\ &= 2\pi(mh.u+mk.v+ml.w),\end{aligned} \tag{7}$$

where (u, v, w) are the co-ordinates of the atom (x, y, z), expressed as fractions of the corresponding sides of the unit cell of the lattice. This important expression for the phase is quite general, and applies equally to oblique axes. It enables us at once, if we know the co-ordinates of the atoms in the unit, to write down the relative phases of their contributions to any spectrum. In practice, it is usual to denote a spectrum by hkl, the indices being then understood to be the Miller indices multiplied by the order, or the numbers mh, mk, ml, in equation (7). In what follows, we shall adopt this convention.

THE STRUCTURE-AMPLITUDE

For each of the N atoms in the unit of structure, there will be a corresponding (hkl) plane, the phase for a reflexion from which can be calculated, in the way just described, from the co-ordinates of the atom, which we will suppose known. The problem now to be solved is to find the resultant amplitude of the wave reflected from the complex of N planes. The relative phases are known, and if we know the amplitude of the wave reflected from each plane, the resultant amplitude can be written down at once from the usual formula for combining simple harmonic waves having the same frequency but different amplitudes and phases. This resultant amplitude, it will be remembered, is given by the length of the side closing a polygon whose other sides are equal in length to the amplitudes of the waves whose resultant is required, the side representing any one component wave making an angle with some fixed direction equal to the phase of that component. Let the amplitude scattered per atom by the planes of the kind A alone in the direction considered be denoted by A, that by planes of the kind B by B, and so on. Let the phases for the reflexions from the different planes, calculated from (7), be ϕ_A, ϕ_B, ... Then, if S is the resultant amplitude per unit of the structure scattered in the direction of the *hkl* spectrum, the phase-amplitude polygon gives at once

$$S^2=(A\cos\phi_A+B\cos\phi_B+\dots)^2 \\ +(A\sin\phi_A+B\sin\phi_B+\dots)^2. \qquad (8)$$

The quantity S is called the **structure-amplitude.** It is a measure of the amplitude reflected per unit of the crystal structure from one of the complex groups of N planes in the direction of the *hkl* spectrum. The groups repeat at intervals D and, in the directions of the spectra, the contributions of all the groups are in phase, so that the total amplitude reflected by all the planes will be proportional to S, and the intensity to S^2.[1]

[1] It should be noticed that the assumption that the total reflected intensity is proportional to S^2 is equivalent to the assumption that the contribution to the total amplitude from each atomic plane is unaffected by the presence of the other planes. The radiation reflected by one set of planes is scattered to some extent by the others before emerging from the crystal. This effect, which is most marked for intense reflexions, modifies the formula for the reflected intensity, but not, of course, the amplitude reflected from a single group of planes corresponding to a crystal unit.

The phase δ of the resultant reflexion, relative to that of the reflexion from a plane through the origin, is given by

$$\tan\delta=(A\sin\phi_A+B\sin\phi_B+\ldots)/(A\cos\phi_A+B\cos\phi_B+\ldots). \quad (9)$$

If the crystal has a symmetry centre, and if this is chosen as origin, the atoms occur in pairs, for every atom with a given phase ϕ there is a corresponding atom with a phase $-\phi$; the sine terms in the expression for S^2 vanish, and we are left with

$$S=2A\cos\phi_A+2B\cos\phi_B+. \quad (10)$$

The resultant phase is in this case either 0 or π. It is often possible to use the expression in this form, but it must always be remembered that this implies the existence of a symmetry centre, and its choice as origin. If the crystal has no symmetry centre, or if some other point is chosen as origin, the full expression for S must be used.

The quantities A, B, . . . in equations (8), (9) and (10) are evidently proportional to the average amplitude scattered by single atoms of the kinds considered in the direction of the spectrum. If the relative scattering powers of the atoms and their positions in the unit cell are known, we can calculate S, and hence the amplitude of the *hkl* spectrum, in terms of the amplitude which it would have had, had all the atoms in the unit been concentrated in a single plane. Conversely, if we measure the relative intensities of the different spectra, we may, by examining the way in which they vary, be able to determine the co-ordinates of the atoms. All methods for determining the structures of complex crystals are based on this idea.

DETERMINATION OF THE SPACE-LATTICE

We shall now apply the formulae developed in the preceding section to the determination of the space-lattice upon which a structure is built. Suppose, for example, that we are investigating a crystal of orthorhombic or cubic symmetry, and that we have already determined the size of the unit cell. We shall naturally have chosen orthorhombic or cubic axes, but, as we have already seen on page 36, it does not follow that the translations of the true space-lattice are parallel to these axes. It is easiest to consider a special case, and we shall take the body-centred cubic lattice, consisting of a point at each corner of a cube and one at the centre. Whatever the structure of the crystal may be, similar groups of atoms are associated with each of the lattice points, and, for our present purpose, we may simply assume that at each

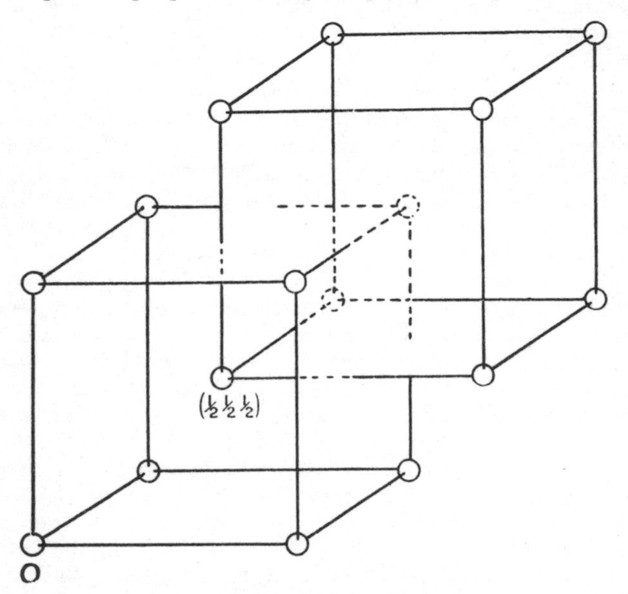

FIG. 21. Body-centred cubic lattice

cube corner and centre there is a similar scattering unit. The crystal is cubic, and we shall have chosen cubic axes. From this point of view, the lattice must be considered as two interpenetrating simple cubic lattices, the corners of one lying at the centres of the other (Fig. 21). The lattice can be thought of as consisting of two similar scattering units associated with each point of a simple cubic lattice. Let us express the co-ordinates of these two units as fractions of the lattice spacings, and work out the structure amplitude in the way described above. We take one point of the lattice as origin; its co-ordinates are then (000), the co-ordinates of the second point which lies at the centre of the cell are then $(\frac{1}{2}\frac{1}{2}\frac{1}{2})$, expressed as fraction of the lattice spacings. The phases for the (hkl) planes corresponding to the two scattering units are then, by (7), 0 and $(h+k+l)\pi$. The expression for S therefore becomes, by (8),

$$S=R\{1+\cos(h+k+l)\pi\},$$

R being the amplitude scattered by a single lattice unit. Now S vanishes whenever $(h+k+l)$ is odd. The intensities of all spectra for which h, k, l satisfy this condition are therefore zero.

Let us consider a little more carefully what this means. We have taken cubic axes, and have determined the distances parallel to these three axes in which the structure repeats itself, these of course being all equal in this case. This gives a cubic unit cell and, on this, the spacings, and the indices hkl of the spectra are based. If the cell is also the true space-lattice cell of the structure, spectra representing all values of hkl should appear. If the lattice is body-centred, we must associate with each unit of the simple lattice a second similar unit lying at the centre of the cell. The presence of this second unit in this very special position causes certain systematic vanishings of the spectra. Certain spectra which would appear if the lattice were simple cannot appear if it is centred. These spectra are those for which $(h+k+l)$ is odd. It is evident at once that the one lattice centring the other halves the spacings of the planes parallel to the cube faces, so that 100, 300, 500 ..., and the corresponding spectra from the other cube faces, cannot occur, for halving a spacing always causes the odd orders corresponding to the original spacing to vanish. It will be seen that these are special cases of the general condition for absent spectra deduced above. It is important to notice, however, that, in determining the space-lattice, attention should be directed to the general spectra, for which none of the indices h, k, l, is zero. Halvings of planes for which one or more of the indices is zero can occur for other reasons, as we shall see below. If the lattice is body-centred, not only spectra of the type 100, 300, ... etc., must vanish, but also 111, 333, 555 ..., 221, 223 ..., and so on. The results we have obtained are of course true for a body-centred lattice of any type, and not only for a body-centred cubic lattice.

In a similar way, a face-centred lattice can be considered as consisting of four interpenetrating primitive lattices, and calculation of the structure-amplitude shows that no spectra can occur for which the indices are partly odd and partly even, but only those for which they are all even or all odd. For each space-lattice there are characteristic absences of spectra of general type, and from these the space-lattice is determined.

THE DETERMINATION OF THE SPACE-GROUP

Just as a space-lattice is characterized by absences of spectra of a general type, so the space-group is characterized by absences of spectra of special types. In a work of this nature, we cannot do more than indicate the principles underlying the determination of space-groups. We shall again consider a structure based on a simple orthorhombic space-lattice, with each point of which is associated a crystal unit. The existence of a lattice of this sort is shown, as we have seen, by the fact that spectra of all general types occur. Suppose now that perpendicular to the (100) face of the lattice we add a 2-fold screw axis. The existence of such an axis necessitates the existence of other units of structure, derived from those already present by a rotation of 180° about the axis, and a translation, parallel to it, of half the a spacing. A set of planes is thus interleaved half-way between the (100) planes of the lattice, the a spacing is halved, and the spectra 100, 300, ..., corresponding to the space-lattice, vanish. In general a 2-fold screw axis must halve the spacing of the lattice in a direction parallel to itself. In a similar way, glide planes of symmetry produce characteristic halvings. A glide plane parallel to (100), with a glide of $b/2$, must halve the b, or (010), spacing; if the glide is $b/2+c/2$, both the b and c, or (010) and (001), spacings are halved (Fig. 22). Glide planes and screw axes are always parallel to special directions in the lattice, so that it is the spectra with some indices zero which are affected by them, and it is this fact which makes it important to consider the general spectra in determining the **space-lattice.** Space-groups exist, which are still based on a simple orthorhombic lattice, for which (100), (010) and (001) are all halved by the action of glide planes and screw axes, and all the odd orders from these planes must be absent: but all the general spectra will still occur, as they should for a simple lattice.

For each of the 230 space-groups the characteristic absent spectra have been worked out, and they are tabulated in

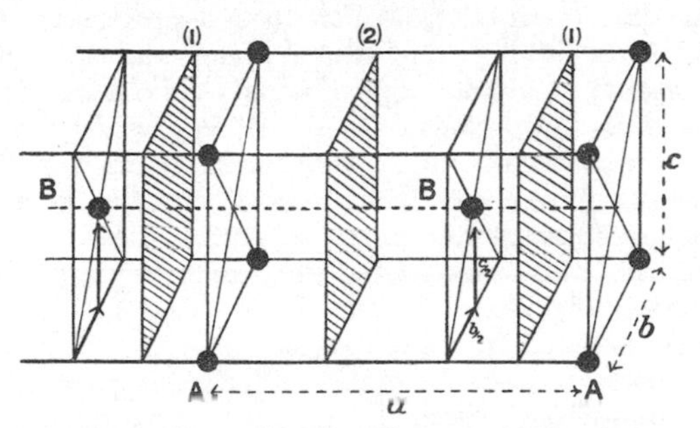

FIG. 22. Illustrating the effect of a glide plane

The shaded planes (1) are glide planes parallel to (100), with a translation $b/2+c/2$. They turn the points A into the points B, thus halving the b and c spacings. It will be seen that the presence of the glide planes (1) necessitates the existence of the glide planes (2) half-way between them

such works as those of Niggli, and Astbury and Yardley, or the International Crystal Tables, which also give all the symmetry elements of the groups. If it is known to which of the 32 crystal classes the crystal under examination belongs, it is generally possible to determine the space-group uniquely from the absent spectra. If the class is uncertain, there may still be some doubt. For example, all crystals give identical reflexions from opposite faces, although these faces may have different properties. In other words, polar and non-polar classes cannot be distinguished by X rays, and unless the crystallographic evidence can decide between them, there will be doubt as to the space-group.

THE LIMITATIONS OF PURELY GEOMETRICAL METHODS

At this point it will perhaps be of advantage to summarize the results we have so far obtained. We have seen that the external forms and symmetry, and the general physical properties of crystals, suggest that they are built up by the repetition of similar units in a 3-dimensional pattern. Crystallographers had recognized this, and had worked out completely the geometry, and possible symmetry of such patterns. A test of the theory became possible with the discovery of the diffraction of X rays by crystals. It was found that the diffraction effects which occur are precisely those to be expected from a 3-dimensional lattice, and this provided at once a way of measuring the actual intervals in which the pattern in a crystal repeats itself. It became plain that the units of the pattern were of atomic or molecular dimensions, and the possibility was opened up of determining in detail the arrangement of the atoms in solid bodies. Let us see how far the arguments of the preceding chapters have led us toward this end.

We have seen that, if suitable material is available, we can always determine the size of the unit cell, using, for example, the rotating crystal method. Once the size and the axes of the unit cell have been fixed, we can determine the **space-lattice** upon which the structure is based, by examining a large number of spectra, and noticing systematic absences of spectra of a general type. Again, by looking for absences of spectra of special types, having one of the indices zero, it is usually possible to determine the **space-group,** the scaffolding of symmetry planes and axes upon which the structure is built. For determining the space-lattice and space-group, oscillation or Weissenberg photographs are generally used. The size of the unit cell, and the density and chemical composition of the crystal, enable us to determine the number of atoms in the unit of structure, and this, together with a knowledge of the space-group, often allows us to limit the possible positions of the atoms. To any position in the unit cell there correspond a number of equivalent positions, derived from the first by the symmetry operations of the space-group. Let us suppose, for example, that this number is eight. Now if we find that there are only four atoms of a given kind in the unit cell, it is evident that they cannot lie at the most general positions, but must lie in some special positions whose equivalence is only four. Such special positions will be on symmetry centres, reflexion planes, or 2-fold rotation-axes: for the image of a point lying on a reflexion plane coincides with itself; if the point moves off the plane, it immediately becomes two points, one the reflexion of the other, and similar considerations apply to the 2-fold axis and the symmetry centre. In this way it is often possible to limit the positions of the atoms considerably, but it is not, in general, possible to fix them. An atom in space requires three co-ordinates, or **parameters,** to fix it. By determining that it must lie on a definite plane or axis, we reduce this number to two or one respectively, but, so far as symmetry alone is concerned, the atom may lie anywhere on the plane or axis, and the remaining parameters may have any values.

Up to this point, the whole process is a geometrical one. There are difficulties, but they are difficulties of technique, and not of principle. Given suitable material, so that the spectra may be observed adequately, it is always possible to determine the unit cell, and generally the space-group. It is, however, the task of X-ray crystallography to find the exact positions of the atoms, and at this point the subject ceases to be a branch of geometry, for we have seen that such a determination must depend on a knowledge of the intensities of the spectra, and both in measuring and in interpreting these, difficulties not of a geometrical, but of a physical nature, arise, and it is with these that we must now concern ourselves.

CHAPTER IV

THE INTENSITIES OF X-RAY SPECTRA

MEASUREMENT OF INTENSITIES

ALTHOUGH the structure of simple crystals can sometimes be inferred with reasonable certainty if the intensities of comparatively few spectra are approximately known, it is not possible to analyse the more complicated structures without an accurate knowledge of at least the relative intensities of a large number of spectra, and it is of great advantage to know their absolute intensities.

It is important to understand what is meant by the intensity of a spectrum in this connexion. We might set the crystal so as to give the maximum reflexion for the spectrum under consideration, and take this as measuring its intensity, but it is found in practice that this procedure does not give consistent results. The state of perfection of crystals of the same substance varies from specimen to specimen. A real crystal is generally far from perfect, and may be thought of as made up of little blocks, or domains. The planes in any one such block are parallel, but their directions differ slightly from block to block, and may be spread over a range of a few minutes of arc, or, in extreme cases, a degree or more. If such a crystal is rotated through the position in which it reflects most strongly, reflexion will persist over a range of angles that depends on the state of perfection. A curve showing the reflected intensity as a function of the angle of reflexion has a maximum, the height of which is greater the narrower the range of reflexion. On the other hand, for a given spectrum, the area under the curve remains nearly constant from one specimen to another, and it is this, the **integrated reflexion,** as it is called, that is taken as a measure of the intensity.

Suppose a beam of X rays of power P to fall at a glancing

angle θ on to a crystal face, which intercepts it completely. Let the power in the reflected beam be $PR(\theta)$. Now suppose the angle θ to vary over the range of reflexion. The integral of the reflected power with respect to the glancing angle θ, divided by the incident power P, is defined as the integrated reflexion from the crystal face.

If the integrated reflexion is denoted by ρ, we may write

$$\rho = \int R(\theta) d\theta. \tag{11}$$

The dimensions of ρ are those of a pure number, as is apparent from the definition.

A rather different case, and a very important one in practice, is that in which a beam of X rays of **intensity** I_0, i.e. a beam in which the energy passing per unit area per unit time is I_0, falls on a very small crystal, bathing it completely in radiation. The **power** in the reflected beam, i.e. the energy reflected per unit time, we write as $I_0 R'(\theta)$. The integrated reflexion is now the integral of the reflexion coefficient $R'(\theta)$ with respect to θ, divided by the incident intensity. Its mathematical form is the same as that for reflexion at a face, but it now has the dimensions of length squared.

In making use of the observed intensities to determine structures it is necessary to employ theoretical formulae for the integrated reflexion, and it was important in the development of the subject to check these for crystals having structures so simple that even approximate intensity measurements were enough to determine them. In the earliest experiments of this kind crystals of rock-salt were used. To determine an absolute integrated reflexion from a crystal face, the crystal is mounted on the table of an X-ray spectrometer, the ionization chamber being set at the correct angle to receive the spectrum, with slits open wide enough to receive the whole reflected beam. The chamber is kept fixed, and the crystal is rotated with uniform angular velocity ω through the reflecting range. The crystal takes a time $d\theta/\omega$ to rotate through the small angular range $d\theta$, and P is the energy incident in unit time. If E is the total energy reflected from the crystal during the passage through the reflecting range

$$E = P\int R(\theta)\frac{d\theta}{\omega},$$

or

$$\rho = \int R(\theta)\, d\theta = \frac{E\omega}{P}. \qquad (12)$$

The absolute integrated reflexion may therefore be determined by measuring the ratio of E, the total energy reflected during the rotation, to P the power in the incident beam, which in turn can be measured by allowing the incident beam to pass directly into the ionization chamber for a known time. The direct radiation from the target of an X-ray bulb contains a continuous background of radiation, as well as the monochromatic characteristic radiation for which alone the integrated reflexion is to be determined. It is therefore necessary to make the incident beam monochromatic by reflecting it from a good crystal, such as calcite, before allowing it to fall on the crystal under investigation. The doubly reflected beam is weak, and with an ionization spectrometer it is possible to make absolute measurements only of fairly strong spectra. Other reflexions may be compared, using the direct beam from the bulb, with a standard spectrum, for example, rock-salt 400, which has been measured absolutely. The integrated reflexion for this spectrum is about 10^{-4}, although it varies somewhat from crystal to crystal. The 200 spectrum is some five times as strong, but it is not a good standard, because it is very subject to the extinction effects to be discussed below. Using a Geiger-counter spectrometer, it is possible to make absolute determinations of much weaker spectra.

In a modification of this method a very small crystal, completely bathed in the radiation, is oscillated backwards and forwards through the reflecting range, the reflected beam being received in a Geiger counter, which must be screened from direct radiation. The counter is connected to a suitable counting-rate meter and scaler, and the number of counts during a given time of oscillation is determined, appropriate correction being made for 'lost counts'. In this way it is possible to measure with considerable accuracy the relative integrated reflexions for a large number of spectra from the small crystal.

PHOTOGRAPHIC METHODS

To make a complete set of observations with a Geiger-counter spectrometer, although it is probably the best way of obtaining a reliable set of relative intensities, is nevertheless a rather lengthy operation, and for most purposes the observations are made photographically, by means of the oscillation camera or the Weissenberg camera. The integrated reflexion is then proportional to the total blackening of the spot on the photographic film corresponding to the spectrum. Various forms of integrating photometer have been devised to measure this total blackening, but it has been found that, for many purposes, relative intensities may be estimated visually with sufficient accuracy. A film marked with a set of spots of graduated intensity, produced by a graduated set of exposure times, is used for comparison. Such estimates can only be made accurately if the blackening of the spots to be compared is not too great. If a large range of intensities has to be dealt with, it is necessary to take a series of photographs, with short exposures for the strong spectra and long exposures for the weak ones, but with a number of spectra of the right blackness for measurement common to successive films, so that the necessary factors for putting all the measurements on the same scale can be determined. A range of intensities of 1,000 to 1 is by no means uncommon in work of this kind.

THEORETICAL FORMULAE FOR INTENSITIES OF REFLEXION

Any formula for the intensity of a spectrum must contain factors of two types, one depending on the nature of the atoms in the unit cell and their arrangement, and the other on the condition of the crystal and the method used in observing the spectrum.

The condition of the crystal is of great importance. Darwin, as early as 1914, showed that a crystal with very small absorption, whose atoms were arranged in mathematically exact array, would reflect X rays totally over a small range of angles, of the order of a few seconds, and that the reflexion would be complete in the first few tens of thousands of lattice planes.[1] Experiment shows, however, that, from nearly all real crystals, the integrated reflexion is perhaps twenty or thirty times stronger than that to be expected from Darwin's perfect-crystal formula. The reason for this was pointed out by Darwin himself. Natural crystals are not as a rule mathematically perfect over any considerable volume. It is more correct to regard them as mosaics of more or less perfect blocks, which, although nearly parallel, may vary in orientation over a small range of angles. It is possible to carry out the calculation for the integrated reflexion from a crystal supposed to consist of blocks so small that there is no appreciable absorption of the rays in any one of them. A crystal of this type is called by Ewald a 'mosaic' crystal. It is easy to see that the integrated reflexion from a mosaic crystal will be much greater than that from a perfect crystal of the same kind, for in the latter, the reflexion all occurs in the first few thousand layers, which screen the lower layers during reflexion. When the angle of reflexion is passed, the rays again penetrate more deeply, but, since the lower layers are exactly parallel to the upper ones, their chance of reflecting is gone. In the mosaic crystal, since the different blocks are not all exactly parallel, each gets its chance of reflecting in turn.

Real crystals are neither ideally perfect nor ideally mosaic. The individual perfect blocks of the mosaic may be so large that the upper layers screen the lower ones **in the same block,** and even if this does not occur, some of the lower blocks will be parallel to the upper ones, and will thus be screened during reflexion. These effects are known as **primary** and **secondary extinction,** respectively, and both

[1] This result is arrived at by taking into account the interaction of each atom with the radiation scattered by the others, instead of treating each as an independent scatterer. This is necessary, because, in a perfect crystal, there will be definite phase relationships between the radiation scattered by the different atoms.

increase the apparent absorption coefficient of the crystal for X rays during reflexion. Most crystals approach much more nearly to the mosaic than to the perfect type, and it is usual to employ the mosaic formula, and to apply an estimated correction to the absorption coefficient to allow for extinction. It would lead us too far to discuss this correction. No method yet devised is entirely satisfactory, and extinction is the greatest difficulty in the way of interpreting quantitative crystal measurements. It affects strong spectra much more than weak ones. Extinction can be avoided by using powdered crystals, but the powder method can only be used effectively when the crystal has high symmetry.

The integrated reflexion from a mosaic crystal of volume dv, so small that absorption within it is negligible, may be written

$$\rho = Q\, dv, \tag{13}$$

and the corresponding expression for reflexion from the face of a mosaic crystal of linear absorption coefficient μ is

$$\rho = Q/2\mu. \tag{14}$$

In both these formulae

$$Q = \frac{N^2\lambda^3}{\sin 2\theta}\,|S|^2\,\frac{1+\cos^2 2\theta}{2}, \tag{15}$$

in which N is the number of crystal units per unit volume, λ the wave-length of the X rays, and θ the glancing angle of reflexion. The factor $(1+\cos^2 2\theta)/2$ allows for the fact that the incident radiation is assumed to be unpolarized in deducing the formula. S is the structure-amplitude per unit cell (p. 48).

THE ATOMIC SCATTERING POWER AND ITS CALCULATION

We have seen above how it is possible to measure the absolute value of the integrated reflexion. If the value so obtained is substituted in formulae (14) and (15), S, the amplitude scattered by a single crystal unit, may be calculated, and by comparing this 'observed' S with the values calculated from different assumed atomic arrangements, the structure of the crystal may be determined. Our next task, therefore, is the theoretical calculation of S.

We must suppose the scattering to be done by the electrons in the atoms. Let us take as the unit scattered amplitude that scattered by a single classical electron, that is to say, one which scatters according to the formula of Sir J. J. Thomson. We are not concerned for the moment with the question as to whether or not such an electron exists; we merely take it as a convenient unit. If the crystal unit consisted of a single electron of this type, the factor S would be $-e^2/mc^2$, e being the charge on an electron expressed in electrostatic units, m its mass, and c the velocity of light. We may take the amplitude, S, scattered by the actual unit in the direction considered as F times that scattered by a single electron, or $-Fe^2/mc^2$. F is a dimensionless number, and is a function of θ, depending both on the distribution of electrons in the individual atoms, and on the arrangement, or parameters, of the atoms themselves.

Suppose now, that the average amplitude scattered by a single atom of a particular kind in the unit is f times that scattered by a classical electron. The total amplitude, F, scattered by the whole unit is obtained by adding together the contributions from the single atoms, taking into account the phase differences introduced by their distribution in the unit cell. We have already seen, in Chapter III, how this allowance for phase is made, and it will be evident from formula (8) that we may write

$$F^2=(f_A \cos \phi_A+f_B \cos \phi_B+\ldots)^2+(f_A \sin \phi_A+f_B \sin \phi_B+\ldots)^2$$

where $f_A, f_B, \ldots$ are the scattering powers for the atoms of kind $A, B, \ldots$, and the phases $\phi_A, \phi_B, \ldots$ are given by equation (7).

It is convenient to write F in the complex form

$$F=\sum_N f_N \cos \phi_N+i\sum_N f_N \sin \phi_N=A+iB, \qquad (16)$$

which includes both the intensity and the phase δ of the spectrum.

We may write

$$|F|^2=A^2+B^2, \qquad \tan \delta=B/A. \qquad (17)$$

The importance of the phase of the resultant will be clear in the next chapter.

Just as the value of F depends on the distribution of the atoms in the unit cell, so f depends on the distribution of the electrons in the atoms. Let us consider an atom of atomic number Z as consisting of a cloud of Z classical electrons surrounding the nucleus. It is the region occupied by these electrons which constitutes the main bulk of the atom, and from which the X-ray scattering takes place. The diameters of the atoms are of the same order of magnitude as the spacings of the crystal planes, and are in general several times the wave-length of the X rays. It will therefore be necessary to take into account the phase differences between the contributions to the scattered beam from electrons in different parts of the atom.

We are of course only concerned with the average scattering from a huge number of atoms, and we shall suppose an average atom of the kind considered to have spherical symmetry, an assumption which is justified by experiment. We may define the average electron density in the atom in the following way. Let $U(r)dr$ be the probability of finding an electron between radii r and $r+dr$ from the centre of the atom. Then $U(r)$ is called the **radial electron-density,** and, since the atom is supposed to be spherically symmetrical, it is a function of r only. $U(r)dr$ gives the average number of electrons lying between distances r and $r+dr$ from the centre of the atom, and we must therefore have $\int_0^\infty U(r)dr = Z$, the total number of electrons in the atom.

Suppose the atom to lie with its centre at O (Fig. 23) on a crystal plane, and consider its contribution to a spectrum formed by reflexion at a glancing angle θ from the plane. It is clear that the radiation contributing to this spectrum has been scattered by the atom through an angle 2θ. The radiation scattered by an electron at A, distant x from the plane, differs in phase from that scattered by electrons lying in the plane by $4\pi x (\sin \theta)/\lambda$. Now x may be greater than λ, so that the phase difference between the contributions to the scattered beam from different parts of the atom may be considerable, if the angle θ is at all large. If $\theta=0$, all the scattered

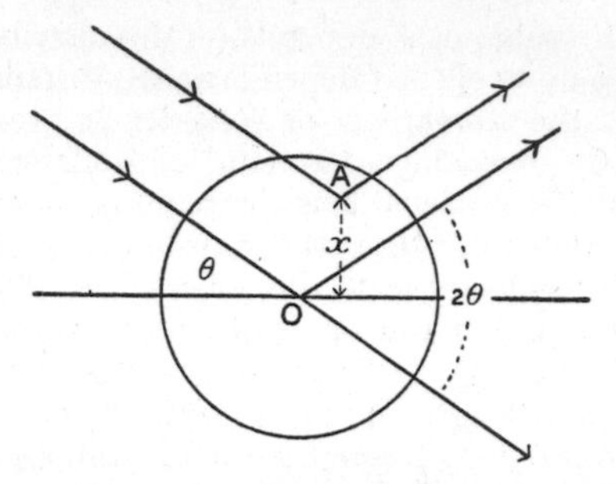

FIG. 23. The scattering of radiation from an atom

components have travelled equal paths. The contributions from all the electrons are then in phase, and the total scattered amplitude is Z times that scattered from a single electron in the same direction, but as θ increases, the phase difference increases also, the contributions from the different parts of the atom no longer co-operate, and the total amplitude scattered is less than Z times that due to a single electron. The factor f therefore approaches the total number of electrons in the atom for small angles of scattering, but decreases rapidly as the angle of scattering increases.

THE f-FACTOR AND WAVE MECHANICS

In order to calculate f theoretically, we need to know $U(r)$, the radial electron density. Now we have expressed $U(r)$ in terms of classical electrons, and we know from the existence of the Compton effect that electrons do not scatter X rays entirely according to classical laws. According to the wave mechanics, instead of thinking of point electrons, describing orbits in the atom, we must consider a wave-function, ψ, a solution of Schrödinger's equation, associated with each point of the atom, and such that $|\psi|^2 dv$ is proportional to the chance of finding an electron in an element of volume dv at the point considered. The quantity $|\psi|^2$ may thus be thought of, in a sense, as the average charge density at any point in the atom, and the quantum theory of scattering shows that, to a close approximation, with radiation of the frequency we are considering here, we may obtain the coherent scattering from the atom, that is to say, the scattered radiation which can interfere and produce X-ray spectra, as distinct from the incoherent Compton radiation which cannot, by treating the quantity $|\psi|^2 dv$ for each element of volume of the atom as an element of classically scattering charge. Thus we may replace the hypothetical distribution of classical electrons, in terms of which f was defined, by the Schrödinger charge-density distribution for the atom. We may in fact put $U(r)$ equal to $4\pi r^2|\psi|^2$, and carry out the calculation of f exactly as if $U(r)$ were a classical distribution of charge. It is quite easy to show that, for such a distribution,

$$f=\int_0^\infty U(r)\frac{\sin\phi}{\phi}dr, \text{ where } \phi=4\pi r(\sin\theta)/\lambda. \qquad (18)$$

Now Hartree has devised a method of calculating the approximate numerical value of $|\psi|^2$ for any point of an atom. If then the theory outlined above is correct, we have a means of calculating f for an atom, and hence, F for any arrangement of atoms.

EXPERIMENTAL TEST OF THE THEORETICAL FORMULAE

It is evidently important to test the theories given above by direct experiment. This has been done by studying quantitatively the reflexion of X rays from certain simple crystals, in which the positions of the atoms are fixed by symmetry, with no undetermined parameters. In rock-salt, which is one of the crystals which was used for this purpose, the Na and Cl atoms lie on two interpenetrating face-centred cubic lattices, and only spectra with indices all odd or all even occur. For spectra with even indices, $F=f_{Cl}+f_{Na}$, and for those with odd indices, $F=f_{Cl}-f_{Na}$. Accurate absolute measurements of the integrated reflexions for a number of spectra were made, and from these the values of F were calculated, using formula (15), and putting $S=Fe^2/mc^2$. The values of F, plotted as a function of θ, lay on two smooth curves, one giving $f_{Cl}+f_{Na}$, the other $f_{Cl}-f_{Na}$. By taking half the sum and half the difference of the ordinates of these curves, f_{Cl} and f_{Na} could be obtained separately as functions of θ. The results were evidently of the right order: the total number of electrons in the two atoms is 28, and $f_{Cl}+f_{Na}$ was about 21 at the smallest angle of scattering at which reflexions were measured, about 12° 30′, and was increasing with decreasing angle; but before the proper comparison between theory and experiment could be made, it was necessary to allow for the thermal motions of the atoms.

THE TEMPERATURE FACTOR

Values of f calculated from theoretical charge distributions will of course refer to the atom at rest; the atoms in a crystal are not, however, at rest, but in a state of thermal vibration. The higher the temperature, the greater the average distance of the electrons in an atom from the lattice planes, and the more rapidly, therefore, the value of f dies away with increasing angle of scattering. If each atom be supposed to vibrate as a whole, it can be shown that $f=f_0e^{-M}$, where f_0 is the value of f for the atom at rest, and

$$M=8\pi^2\overline{u^2}(\sin^2\theta)/\lambda^2, \qquad (19)$$

$\overline{u^2}$ being the mean square displacement of the atoms from the average position of the planes at which reflexion is taking place at a glancing angle θ. Debye and Waller have given expressions for $\overline{u^2}$, for simple crystals, in terms of the temperature, and known quantities, such as the specific heats and elastic constants, so that for such crystals it is possible to calculate the value of M.

Experiments on the variation with temperature of the intensity of reflexion of X rays from NaCl showed that, from about 500° abs. down to the lowest temperature used, that of liquid air at 86° abs., the observed temperature factor agreed excellently with that calculated from Waller's theory. This being so, it seems justifiable to extrapolate further, and to calculate from the observed values of f the values at the absolute zero. We must not, however, assume that the values so calculated are those for the atom at rest. The wave-mechanics requires that the atoms in a lattice should possess, as Planck had already suggested, half a quantum of vibrational energy for each degree of freedom, even at the absolute zero, and it will therefore be necessary to apply a further correction to the f values corrected to this temperature, in order to allow for the existence of this zero-point energy. It is possible to make this correction, and, by so doing, we obtain a set of values of f_0 which can be compared with those calculated theoretically.

The values of $U(r)$ for Na^+ and Cl^- were calculated by Hartree from the wave-functions of the atoms,[1] and in Fig. 24 they are shown, plotted against the atomic radius r. From these, the values of f_0 were calculated by integrating equation (18) numerically. The theoretical f curves for Na^+ and Cl^- are shown by the full lines in Fig. 25; the circles in the same figure represent the observed values of f, corrected, as just described, with allowance for zero-point energy, and the crosses, the same values without the allowance for zero-point energy. It will be seen that the agreement between theory and experiment is, on the whole, excellent if zero-point energy be assumed. Equally good agreement has been obtained with similar experiments on KCl and Al, and, so far as the evidence goes at present, the theory given above appears to be confirmed quantitatively by experiment, and can therefore be used with some confidence as a basis for structure determination.

THE AMPLITUDES OF THE ATOMIC VIBRATIONS

From the values of M, it is possible to calculate directly the root-mean-square displacements of the atoms from their mean positions. The following values are obtained at room temperature. In NaCl, Na, 0·24 Å, Cl, 0·22 Å; in KCl, K and Cl, 0·25 Å; in Al, 0·17 Å. At the absolute zero, the amplitudes in NaCl and KCl are still about 0·1 Å, a by no means negligible fraction of the lattice spacings.

[1] The wave functions and the theoretical values of f are calculated on the assumption that the atoms are ionized. This, as we shall see in Chapter VI, is probably the case in the rock-salt lattice. For the ions, the total number of electrons is 10 for Na^+ and 18 for Cl^-.

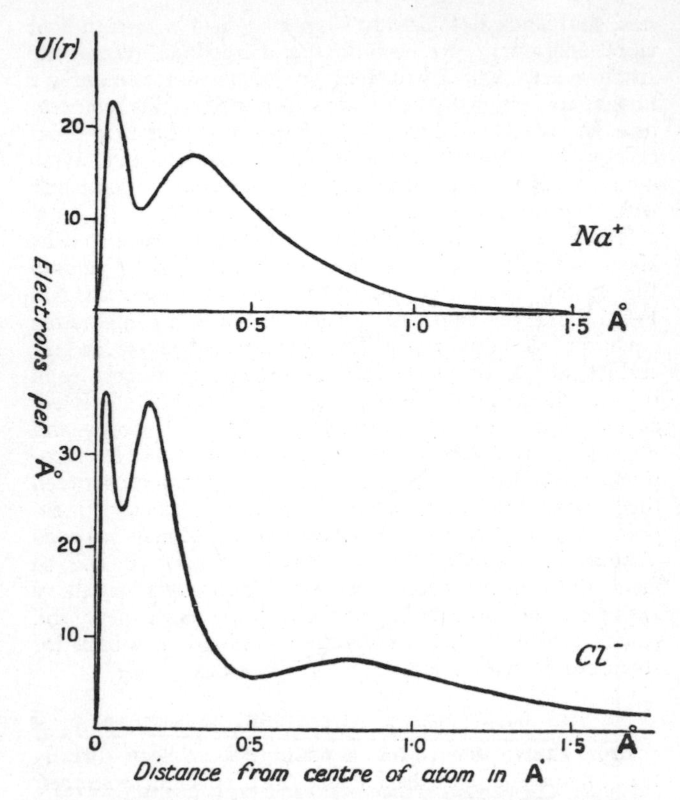

FIG. 24. Radial distributions of charge density in Na^{+} and Cl^{-} (*Hartree*)

DIFFUSE REFLEXIONS DUE TO THERMAL MOVEMENT

A detailed treatment of the effect of thermal motion on diffraction by crystals shows that in addition to reducing the intensity of the spectra, it may cause quite complicated background patterns to develop, from the nature and distribution of which it is sometimes possible to obtain information about the vibrations of the molecules. In particular,

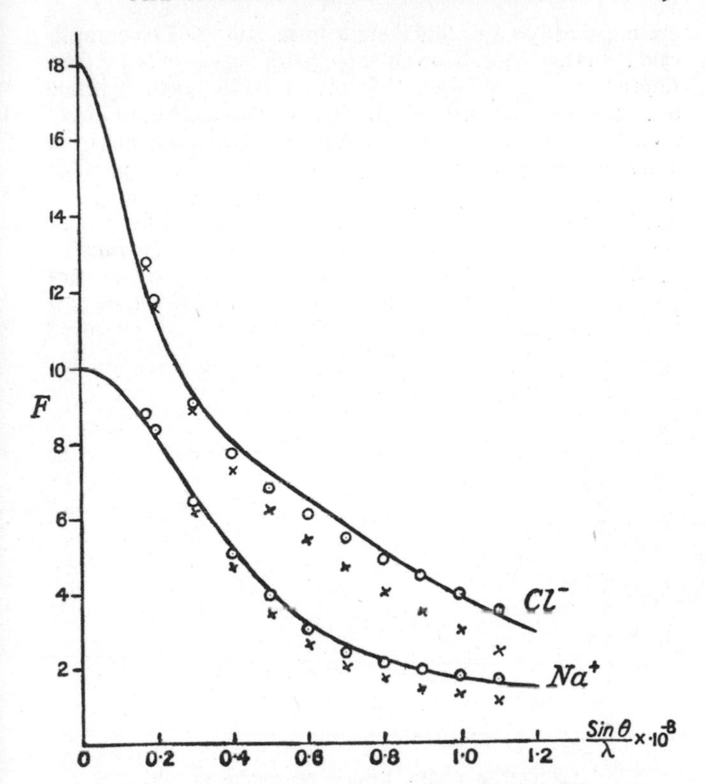

FIG. 25. Comparison of theoretical and experimental f curves

The continuous lines are the f curves calculated from the Schrödinger charge-density distributions for the atoms at rest. The circles and crosses are the observed values corrected for temperature with and without allowance for zero-point energy

diffuse maxima in the same directions as the sharp interference maxima make their appearance and because of their diffuseness, may be recorded on the diffraction photograph even when conditions for the production of the ordinary maxima are not exactly fulfilled. The diffuse patterns are in fact optical 'ghosts' of the same nature as those given by a grating that has a periodic error in its ruling. The complicated thermal vibrations of the crystal lattice may be considered as built up of a set of normal modes, each of which is a wave running through the structure in a definite direction, thus imposing a periodic error on the lattice spacings. There are of course millions of such waves, in all possible directions, so that instead of being discrete spots, the ghosts form a diffuse cloud. Such patterns are particularly well shown by certain organic crystals, because of their relative softness and large thermal movement, but they are of very general occurrence and appear even in the diffraction patterns from diamond.

CHAPTER V

THE DETERMINATION OF THE ATOMIC PARAMETERS

INTRODUCTION

WE are now in a position to discuss the determination of the parameters of a crystal structure. We suppose the integrated reflexions of as complete a set as possible of the spectra given by the crystal to have been determined, preferably absolutely, although, as we have seen, the values available will more usually be relative. The integrated reflexions are proportional to Q of equation (15), and from them, using the known values of N, λ, and θ, we determine a set of numbers proportional to $|S|$, and hence to $|F|$, for the different spectra. These values of $|F|$ will as a rule be relative, and it is desirable, if possible, to put them on an absolute scale. This can often be done with a fair degree of approximation by a method due to Wilson, if the relative values of a large number of spectra are known. The principle of Wilson's method is easy to understand. Equation (17) for $|F|^2$ can be written in the form

$$|F|^2=\sum_n f_n^2+2\sum_{mn} f_n f_m \cos(\phi_n-\phi_m), \qquad (20)$$

where m and n refer to any pair of different atoms in the unit cell. Suppose we average both sides of this equation over all the spectra having values of $\sin\theta$ near a certain value, so that the values of f, which are functions of $\sin\theta$, may be treated as constants. We do not know the values of $\phi_n-\phi_m$, because we do not know the structure, but we can be fairly sure that if an average is taken over a considerable number of spectra the mean of the terms involving the cosines of the phase differences will be small, because approximately equal numbers of positive and negative values are likely to occur.

Thus we can write as an approximation

$$\overline{|F|^2} = \sum_n f_n^2. \qquad (21)$$

The atomic scattering factors, f, for the different atoms have been tabulated, so that it is possible to calculate what the average value of $|F|^2$ should be, and this may be compared with the average of the corresponding quantities proportional to $|F|^2$ determined from the observations. In this way an approximate scaling factor can be obtained for the value of $\sin\theta$ considered. The factor will depend on θ, because it is unlikely that in calculating the value of f^2 a correct allowance will have been made for the temperature factor. The spectra are therefore divided into groups, each of which covers a certain range of $\sin\theta$, and the averaging is done for each group, so that the dependence of the scaling factor on $\sin\theta$ can be approximately determined. At a later stage, when the structure is approximately known, it will be necessary to revise this scaling factor, making use of the calculated values of $|F|^2$ in forming the average, but it is advantageous to obtain an approximate factor in the way described at the outset. For a complete determination of a crystal structure it may be necessary to measure a thousand or more spectra, so that the work involved in the preliminary stages may be considerable. Fortunately, it is not always necessary to use so many spectra, but almost any determination of structure that is at all complicated will involve several hundred.

We may suppose, then, that in some such way as this, we have obtained a very nearly absolute set of $|F|$ values, covering a large range of spectra completely. The next step is to compare these measured values with those calculated from equation (17), assuming likely values of the atomic parameters. The method is essentially one of trial and error. Different atomic arrangements are tried until one is found that gives satisfactory agreement between observed and calculated $|F|$'s over a range so large that it cannot well be accidental. For a crystal with one or two parameters, quite a few trials are usually enough to fix the structure, but if, as is now usually the case, there are ten, twenty, or even more parameters, the problem could not possibly be solved in this way unless certain considerations limited the choice of parameters, and enabled values not far from the truth to be guessed at the outset.

Important, among such considerations, is the idea of atomic size. Information obtained from structures which have been determined shows that each kind of atom in a crystal structure occupies a certain definite amount of room. Proposed structures, which are quite possible so far as symmetry alone is concerned, but in which the atoms have not sufficient room, can thus be discarded at once, and this frequently limits the possible arrangements very greatly, and may sometimes almost determine the structure. It must be remembered also that a crystal is statically stable. If the structure is composed of positive and negative ions, their distribution is likely to be such that each ion is surrounded, so far as possible, by those of opposite sign. It is a very noticeable fact that, when models of structures which have been determined are made, they look stable and reasonable. The question of co-ordination is also very important. Certain atoms are nearly always surrounded by the same number of atoms of a given other kind, arranged in the same way. Important information may often be gained by measuring the three principal refractive indices of the crystal. If the crystal contains flat molecules arranged in sheets, the refractive index for light vibrating parallel to these sheets is likely to be very high, and that for light vibrating perpendicular to them correspondingly low. The diffuse spots due to thermal movement can sometimes give useful information. If the structure is made up of layers of flat molecules, which can usually vibrate with greater amplitude in a direction perpendicular to their planes than in directions lying in them, it can be shown that the diffuse spots associated with the spectra reflected from crystal planes nearly parallel to those of the molecules will be unusually large, and nearly circular in outline. On the other hand, the diffuse spots associated with planes nearly perpendicular to sets of chain-like molecules are likely to be elongated and streak-like in appearance. It is sometimes possible to infer the orientation of the molecules fairly accurately from the diffuse spectra. Measurements of the anisotropy of the magnetic susceptibility of crystals can also sometimes give very accurate estimates of the orientation of the molecules.

By such methods, the skilled worker is able to narrow down the field of possible structures before making any actual tests, but it must be emphasized that such procedure is only provisional, and does not determine the structure. The final determination can only be made by obtaining agreement between the observed and calculated F values.

ANALYSIS BY MEANS OF FOURIER SERIES

A most important method of using the information given by the intensity measurements was suggested originally by Sir William Bragg in 1915, and developed in more detail by Duane, Compton, and Havighurst. It was not until 1929 that W. L. Bragg showed its real power in crystal analysis, but since that time it has become the standard method of attack.

An infinitely extended crystal structure, based on a lattice with translations a, b, c, is periodic in three dimensions, with these periods, and the density of scattering matter within it, now to be thought of as continuously distributed, and as having maxima at the positions of the atoms, must be expressible as a triple Fourier series. It turns out, moreover, that the coefficients of this series are related in a simple way to the amplitudes of the spectra given by the crystal, and that there is one term in the series for each spectrum. If it were possible to determine the Fourier coefficients, the density of scattering matter at any point, and hence the structure, could be determined by summing the series. We have now to see to what extent a direct determination of this kind is possible.

It should be noticed first of all that a crystal of finite size cannot have a truly periodic structure, and that its density is therefore strictly speaking to be represented by a Fourier integral, and not by a Fourier series; but in any crystal large enough to be used experimentally for purposes of analysis there are so many repetitions of the unit of pattern that the error made by representing its density by means of the series is of little or no importance. We shall not here give the formal derivation of the appropriate series, but merely point out the principles upon which it is based.

Consider a distribution of scattering matter the density of which is constant over any plane perpendicular to x, but varies periodically, with a period a, in the direction of x. The density $\rho(x)$ of such a distribution can evidently be represented by a Fourier series of the type

$$\rho(x)=A_0+\sum_n A_n \cos\left(\frac{2\pi nx}{a}+\delta_n\right), \tag{22}$$

consisting of a constant term, plus a set of sinusoidal terms with periods a, $a/2$, . . . a/n . . . Such a distribution of scattering matter can give spectra by reflexion according to Bragg's law. Any one of the sinusoidal distributions will contribute two spectra only, and it will be found that the nth component contributes the two spectra of order $\pm n$. Thus, to each spectrum there corresponds a sinusoidal term in the Fourier series, the period of the term being the fundamental period a divided by the order of the spectrum.

This can be readily extended to three dimensions. The density distribution in the crystal can be thought of as made up of a set of periodic distributions, such as that we have just considered, one for every possible set of atomic planes, the planes of constant density in any such distribution being parallel to the atomic planes to which it corresponds. Each such distribution can then be expressed as the sum of a set of sinusoidal terms, one for each order of spectrum from the planes considered. If $\rho(x, y, z)$ is the density of the scattering matter in the crystal, expressed in electrons per unit volume, it can be shown that

$$\rho(x, y, z)=\frac{1}{V}\sum_{-\infty}^{\infty}\sum_{h}\sum_{k}\sum_{l} F(hkl) \exp\left\{2\pi i\left(\frac{hx}{a}+\frac{ky}{b}+\frac{lz}{c}\right)\right\}. \tag{23}$$

V is here the volume of the unit cell, and $F(hkl)$ the structure factor of the spectrum hkl, and there is one term for every spectrum.

The series has here been written in the complex exponential form (p. 62) in which the coefficients $F(hkl)$ may themselves be complex numbers, containing a phase, which, in equation (22), was included in the argument of the cosine term. We here come upon the principal difficulty in using Fourier series to determine crystal structures; for we have no direct way of measuring the phases of the spectra. Our measurements give us not F but $|F|^2$, and we cannot therefore completely determine the coefficients necessary for summing the series. It is plain from equation (23) that to determine the density it is essential to know the phases of the spectra as well as their amplitudes.

We may look at the matter in another way. The intensities and directions of the spectra produced by a sinusoidal distribution of scattering matter are not altered by moving that distribution perpendicular to the planes of constant density without rotation, which is the geometrical interpretation of changing the phase δ. Any or all of the large number of sinusoidal components from which the density ρ is built up can be so moved relative to one another, entirely altering the density, without in any way altering the direction and the intensities of the spectra. Putting the matter rather differently: there is no unique structure corresponding to the set of intensities that we measure from the crystal, but an infinite number of possible structures. Fortunately, many of these optically possible structures would be physically absurd. We shall usually have some knowledge of the dimensions of the molecules, or at least of the possible interatomic distances, and other information of the kind discussed on page 73, which enables us to limit the possibilities. The preliminary process of trial and error is now seen to be directed towards guessing the phases of enough of the stronger spectra to make it possible to use the Fourier series effectively. If this can be done, the nature of the structure may become clear enough for more of the phases to be determined. The next evaluation of the series will give the structure more closely still, and so by successive refinements the accurate positions of the atoms are determined.

Matters are made much easier if it is known that the crystal unit has a centre of symmetry, for then any Fourier component must have either a maximum or a minimum at the origin, and the phase δ must be either 0 or π. The corresponding phase factor will be either $+1$ or -1, and the series (23) can be written

$$V\rho(x, y, z) = |F(000)| + 2\sum_{hkl} \pm |F(hkl)| \cos\left\{2\pi\left(\frac{hx}{a}+\frac{ky}{b}+\frac{lz}{c}\right)\right\}. \quad (24)$$

We have now therefore to guess only the signs of the coefficients, still often a formidable task, but much easier than determining a set of quite arbitrary phases. The summation is here to be taken over all orders *hkl* of spectra, but positive and negative orders *hkl* and $\bar{h}\bar{k}\bar{l}$ are not to be distinguished. Let us assume for the moment that the signs are known. The next step is to evaluate the Fourier series for enough points (x, y, z) in the unit cell to determine the structure. For a full 3-dimensional determination there may be a thousand or more terms in the series, and it is necessary to carry out the summation for a large number of points. Three-dimensional syntheses are becoming increasingly important as the structures investigated become more complex, but the labour of making them is almost prohibitive unless computing aids are available. Electronic computers are now regularly used in many laboratories, and have greatly increased the range of possible structure-determinations. For a long time, however, the summation of three-dimensional series was practicable only in relatively simple cases, and was rarely undertaken.

TWO-DIMENSIONAL FOURIER PROJECTIONS

Very much less labour is involved if, as was suggested by W. L. Bragg in 1929, the projection of the scattering matter contained in the unit cell on one or more of its faces is determined. This projection is periodic in two dimensions only, and the number of terms involved is usually less than two hundred. Its summation is therefore quite practicable even without the help of calculating machines.

Let $\sigma(x, y)$ be the electron density, in electrons per unit area, of the projection parallel to the *c*-axis of the scattering matter in the unit cell on to the face *ab*. It is then easy to show that

$$A\sigma(x, y) = \sum_h \sum_k F(hk0) \exp\left\{2\pi i\left(\frac{hx}{a} + \frac{ky}{b}\right)\right\}, \tag{25}$$

A being the area of the *ab* face of the cell. Only the spectra belonging to the zone with *l* zero, that is to say, the spectra that appear on the zero layer line in a rotation photograph taken about the *c*-axis, now contribute to the series. There are of course analogous expressions for the projections on the other faces. The series is evaluated for points (x, y), usually at intervals in the co-ordinates of 1/60 of the corresponding sides of the unit cell. The number representing the density, which is the sum of the series for the point (x, y), is plotted at the corresponding point on a diagram representing the face of the cell, and contour lines are then drawn connecting points of equal density. A chart resembling a contour map of a hilly country is obtained, the summits of the hills representing the positions of the atoms projected on to the plane.

Projections of this kind on two of the faces of the cell would determine the positions of the atoms in three dimensions if all the atoms showed clearly, without overlap, in both diagrams. In most actual projections there is a certain amount of overlap, and it is not always possible to fix the atomic positions as closely as could be desired. Nevertheless, if one clear projection can be obtained, and it is surprising how often this is possible, there is usually little doubt about the general features of the molecule. For more accurate work it is desirable to make 3-dimensional determinations, although this involves very much more labour, both in observing the necessary full set of spectra of all indices, and in summing the series. Usually, 2-dimensional projections will be made first, from which the positions of the atoms can be determined with sufficient accuracy to fix most of the phases for the 3-dimensional series. The usual method of procedure is to calculate the density over a series of planes, closely enough spaced to give the configuration of the molecule, or the smallest independent unit of the structure. A contour diagram similar to those for the projections on the faces is drawn for each plane of section, and the accuracy with which the position of the atomic centre can be determined clearly depends on the closeness of the planes.

In Fig. 26 portions of several such plane sections, superposed in the correct relative positions, are shown for one of the molecules in the crystal of *p*-chlor-iodoxy benzene, $Cl(C_6H_4)IO_2$. The IO_2 group lies to the right. Above and

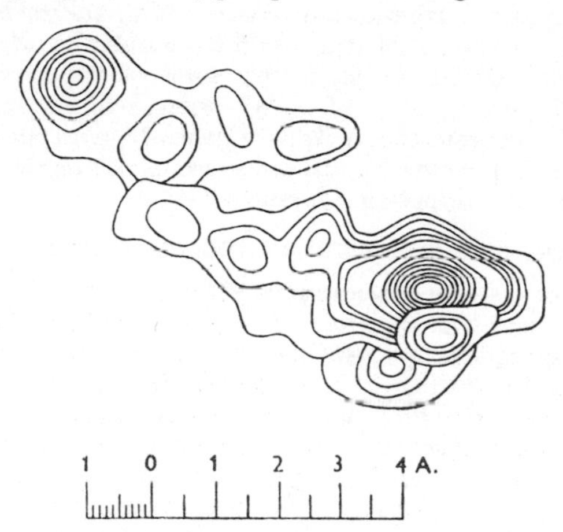

FIG. 26. A molecule of *p*-chlor-iodoxy benzene as shown by 3-dimensional Fourier synthesis (*Archer*)

below the large maximum representing the I atom are sections containing the two O atoms, their bonds to the I atom being nearly at right angles. The benzene ring, the six atoms of which are indicated by weaker maxima, slopes downwards towards the top left-hand corner of the diagram, where the Cl atom lies. To get the carbon positions more accurately, sections at closer intervals would have been necessary.

We return now to the discussion of the 2-dimensional series, which we shall assume applied to a structure having a centre of symmetry. It is not likely that the correct signs of all the coefficients will have been used for the first summation. They are, of course, obtained by assuming a probable structure, and then calculating the structure factors F with the corresponding atomic co-ordinates. The calculated signs and the observed values of $|F|$ are used in the summation. If a good initial estimate of the structure has been made, the positions of the atoms should show out fairly clearly in the first projection, although there will probably be some false detail, and it will be possible to make a revised estimate of the atomic co-ordinates. With the revised co-ordinates a new set of structure factors must be calculated, and it will usually be found that some of the coefficients, generally among those of higher order, will have changed sign. A new projection must then be made, with the revised signs, and, if necessary, this process must be repeated until no significant improvement results.

THE REFINEMENT OF THE FOURIER PROJECTION

The calculation of the structure factors is at best a tedious process, and it is therefore important to reduce the number of successive approximations by using some systematic method of adjusting the co-ordinates determined as a result of a projection before making a new one. There are a number of ways of doing this, but we have only space to consider one, which has been developed by Cochran.

Suppose a projection to have been made, and the values of the atomic co-ordinates to have been estimated from it. Using these co-ordinates and the theoretical values of the atomic scattering factors, f, which relate to spherically symmetrical atoms, we calculate a set of structure factors F_c. Another projection is then made by summing the series with the coefficients $F_0 - F_c$, the difference between the observed and calculated structure factors, instead of F_0. This projection gives the difference between the projection from which the atomic co-ordinates were estimated and one for a crystal in which ideal spherical atoms occupy the positions corresponding to these co-ordinates. If the structure had in fact consisted of ideal atoms occupying these positions, and if all the observations had been ideally accurate, the difference projection would have been zero everywhere. In fact, this will never be so. The actual atoms are not exactly like the ideal atoms used in calculating the structure factors; they are in thermal motion, usually with different amplitudes in different directions; the atomic co-ordinates will probably have been incorrectly estimated from the projection; the observations are not ideally accurate; and, finally, there may perhaps have been hydrogen atoms in the structure, which cannot easily be included in calculating the structure factors.

If the atomic positions have been correctly estimated, but incorrect allowances have been made for thermal movement and the atomic scattering factors, the difference projection will still show peaks and hollows, but the estimated atomic positions will lie at the summits of peaks, or at the bottom of the hollows, or in other words at places where the gradient of the difference contour map is zero. Usually, however, the estimated position will be found to lie somewhere on the slope of one of the hills or hollows. It is not difficult to see that the position of the atom may be adjusted by moving it *up* the slope, and the amount of shift necessary can in fact be estimated from the gradient at the estimated position. In this way, adjustments can be made, if necessary, to all the atomic co-ordinates. With the new co-ordinates, a fresh set of values for F_c must be calculated, and a new difference projection made. If the adjustments of the co-ordinates cause any change of sign in F these must of course be included in calculating the projection. From this new projection, further necessary adjustments of the co-ordinates are estimated, and the process is repeated until further refinement yields no improvement. It is hardly necessary to say that the original projection must be quite a good one for Cochran's method of refinement to be usefully applied, but if this condition is fulfilled, it is undoubtedly a method of great power.

One difficulty of principle in using the Fourier series is that since only a finite number of spectra can be observed, the series must be terminated before the remaining coefficients have become inappreciable. This is exactly equivalent to employing an optical instrument with a limited aperture, and, as always in such cases, it may give rise to false detail in the projection, which is, in effect, an optical image. This false detail is likely to be specially marked if heavy atoms, such as iodine or bromine, occur in the crystal; for the atomic scattering powers of such atoms die away only slowly with increasing order of spectrum, and may contribute considerably to the terms missing from the series. The peaks in the projections corresponding to such atoms are sometimes surrounded by rings of alternately positive and negative density, which are really diffraction rings caused by lack of optical resolution. Such rings may materially affect the positions of the peaks due to neighbouring atoms, and reduce the accuracy of the determination of their position. An advantage of Cochran's method is that it largely gets rid of such effects, for the projection is given by the difference between two Fourier series for which the termination errors will be approximately the same, and will therefore to a large extent cancel out.

The difference projection can also show up thermal movements in a remarkable way. It is usual, before calculating the structure factors, to apply a general correction for thermal movement, assuming this to be the same in all directions, but it may often happen that thermal movements are not spherically symmetrical, but that certain atoms oscillate with a greater amplitude in one direction than in others. If no allowance has been made for this in calculating F_c, the peak corresponding to the atom in the F_0 projection will be spread out in the direction of motion more than that in the F_c projection. In the difference, or F_0-F_c projection, there will therefore be a hollow at the position of the atom, flanked by hills on either side in the direction of the greatest thermal movement. In this way it is possible to study the individual vibration of atoms. A beautiful example of this will be found in a paper by Cochran on the structure of adenine hydrochloride.[1]

In the same paper, the positions of the hydrogen atoms in the molecule are determined, for when all corrections for

[1] W. Cochran, *Acta Crystallographica*, **4**, 81 (1951).

atomic position and thermal movement had been made, the difference projection showed quite clearly peaks corresponding to the hydrogen atoms in the structure, which had not been included in calculating F_c. It is hardly necessary to add that a determination of this degree of refinement presupposes very accurate determinations of intensities.

SOME METHODS OF DETERMINING PHASES

It will be evident from what has been said that it is essential to be able to determine the phases of as many as possible of the spectra before starting on a Fourier synthesis. We have already seen that there is no universal direct method of doing this. Nevertheless, it is sometimes possible to determine the phases of the stronger spectra fairly directly. It may, for example, happen that the structure contains an atom with a large scattering factor, so great that it determines the phases of most of the spectra. If the position of this atom can be determined, the necessary phases can be calculated. It may also sometimes be possible to replace one such atom by another in the same position without disturbing the essential nature of the structure. Then, by observing whether the intensity of a spectrum has been increased or decreased by the resulting change of scattering power, it may be possible to fix its sign. A method of this kind is essentially optical. It is exemplified by Robertson's determination of the structures of the phthalocyanines, still perhaps the most beautiful example of a direct determination.

THE PATTERSON SERIES

Both these methods depend on rather special conditions, and it is important to consider what information can be obtained from a knowledge of the intensities only, without the phases. It cannot give the complete structure, as we have seen, but it must nevertheless tell us something about it. It was pointed out by Patterson that the series

$$P(x, y, z) = \frac{1}{V}\sum_h\sum_k\sum_l |F(hkl)|^2 \cos\left\{2\pi\left(\frac{hx}{a}+\frac{ky}{b}+\frac{lz}{c}\right)\right\}, \qquad (26)$$

in which the squares of the structure factors, which can be

determined directly, are used as coefficients, instead of the structure factors themselves, has interesting properties. The function P, plotted in space, is periodic in a, b, c parallel to x, y, z, and shows maxima at certain points. The vector distance from the origin to any such maximum represents the vector distance between two atoms in the actual structure. It does not tell us whereabouts in the structure the two atoms are, but only the magnitude and direction of the distance between them, or rather that somewhere in the unit cell there are two atoms having this vector separation. The size of the maximum is proportional to the product of the scattering factors of the two atoms involved, so that the method is particularly useful in giving the distances between the heavy atoms in the structure. The peaks in the Patterson distribution are rather diffuse, and it is not easy to interpret for a structure containing a number of light atoms, unless the molecules are known to have a certain symmetry, or to contain certain interatomic distances that repeat themselves, when useful information can sometimes be obtained. If the crystal has known symmetry elements it may be possible by calculating the value of the Patterson function over certain planes or along certain lines to determine directly the distances of the heavier atoms from the symmetry elements and so to fix the atomic positions. If these atoms should determine the phases, we can then proceed directly with the analysis. The Patterson series can be summed directly from the observations, and is a valuable preliminary method of attack, although it cannot be relied upon to give results in every case.

Recently, certain methods introduced by Harker and Kaspar have been developed which may have great possibilities. Although it is not possible to determine the signs of the structure factors of a centro-symmetrical structure experimentally it is nevertheless possible to set up certain relations between them, in the form of inequalities which must be satisfied between structure factors with indices related in certain ways. It may then be found that structure factors of the observed magnitude can only fulfil these relationships in quite a few ways, and possibly in only one way, and thus the signs may be fixed. At present, the method is in use in comparatively few laboratories, but much work is being done on it, and the results are encouraging. If progress is to be made in analysing really complex structures, some rapid and effective method of phase determination is essential.

CHAPTER VI

TYPES OF CRYSTAL STRUCTURE

SIMPLE METALLIC AND IONIC CRYSTALS

IN this chapter we shall consider, very briefly, some of the more important results of crystal analysis. Space will not permit of a detailed description of any particular structures, and we must confine ourselves to the discussion of some of the broader principles which appear to govern the building of crystals. One of the most interesting points is the importance of purely geometrical, as distinct from chemical, considerations. To a close approximation, we may regard each atom as a sphere of definite radius, and may consider crystals to be formed by packing such spheres in the most stable and economical manner. Naturally a statement of this kind requires much qualification, but, as a broad generalization, it is of great importance, and explains many of the salient facts of crystal structure.

In crystals of the metallic elements, the arrangement of the atoms is often simply that of an assemblage of spheres packed as closely as possible. Two types of close-packing are of special importance. Suppose, for example, that we are piling balls on a table, and that the first layer has been completed. If the balls in this layer are tightly packed, their centres will lie at the corners of a network of equilateral triangles. The balls of the second layer must now be placed so as to lie in the hollows of the first layer, and those of the third layer in the hollows of the second. Each layer is, of course, exactly similar, but, in considering the structure as a whole, we see that there are two possibilities for the balls of the third layer: they may be placed exactly over those of the first layer and the structure may then be continued so that pairs of layers repeat indefinitely; or they may be placed neither over the balls of the first layer, nor over those of the second layer, the structure being continued by placing the fourth layer over the first, the fifth over the second, and so on, so that the arrangement of three layers is repeated. The first type of arrangement has hexagonal symmetry. The second has cubic symmetry, and an examination of a model built in this way will show that the centres of the balls lie on a **face-centred** cubic lattice. The packing is equally close in the two types of arrangement, every ball being touched by 12 neighbours. Among the elements which have a face-centred cubic, or cubic close packed, structure are Cu, Ag, Au, Ca, Al, Pb, and Pt. The hexagonal close packed structure is exemplified by Be, Mg, Zn, Cd, Ru, and Os. Not all metallic elements crystallize in a close packed structure. Li, Na, K, Cr, Mo, W and the ordinary modification of Fe, as well as a number of others, have a body-centred cubic structure, while others, among which may be mentioned As, Sb, Bi, S, Se, Te, I, and Mn, have more complicated structures.

It is in the simple inorganic compounds that the geometrical relationships of crystal structure are best shown. The atoms in such crystals are almost certainly ionized, and for this reason they are often called *ionic* crystals. In NaCl, for example, we may suppose that the Na atom has lost its outer electron, and so has acquired an excess of positive charge, while the Cl atom has absorbed the electron lost by the Na atom into its structure, completing the *M* electron group, and at the same time acquiring an excess of negative charge. Two such ions will attract one another, because of the electrostatic forces between their excess charges, but they cannot approach to within less than a certain distance, owing to the strong forces of repulsion which must set in when their outer electron shells come into close proximity. When the centres of the two ions come within a certain distance of one another, attraction and repulsion balance, and they can approach no closer. The repulsive forces increase very rapidly with decreasing distance, once they have become appreciable, so that even a very large increase in the attractive force cannot pull the ions much closer together, and it is in this sense that we must think of them as possessing a definite radius.

We may think of the simple inorganic compounds as built up of such oppositely charged ions, each with its appropriate ionic radius. In order to reduce the electrostatic energy to a minimum, each ion will, so far as possible, surround itself with ions of the opposite sign, but it appears also to be a condition of stability that the anions and kations should touch each other in the sense explained above. Suppose, for example, that a crystal of type AX, A and X being oppositely charged ions, has a structure such that the ions A lie at the centres of cubes formed by the ions X, and the ions X at the centres of cubes formed by the ions A. In such a structure, each ion has eight ions of the opposite sign around it; in other words, the co-ordination number is eight, which is the highest possible for a crystal with equal numbers of the two kinds of ion. Now, merely as a matter of geometry, unless the ratio of the radius of A to that of X is greater than 0·73, the X ions will touch one another along the cube edges and the A ions will, so to speak, 'rattle' inside the cubes of X ions without touching them. Now structures of this kind appear to be unstable, and if the ratio of the radii becomes less than 0·73 the crystals tend to have the rock-salt type of lattice, in which each ion is surrounded by only six of the opposite sign, but in which the anions and kations are again able to touch one another. The alkaline halides provide an interesting example of this. CsI, CsBr and CsCl, in which the radii of the two ions are nearly equal, crystallize in the first of the two forms discussed above, with a co-ordination number of eight, but all the others have a rock-salt structure, with a co-ordination number of six. Most of the oxides and sulphides, and some of the selenides, of the bivalent metals also have a rock-salt structure. If the ratio of the ionic radii is less than 0·41, the larger ions come into contact without touching the smaller ones even in the rock-salt structure. Geometrical stability can again be attained, however, if the co-ordination number sinks to four. This gives the zinc-blende (cubic) or wurtzite (hexagonal) structure, in which each ion lies at the centre of a regular tetrahedron of ions of the opposite kind. CuCl, CuBr, CuI, BeS, ZnS, ZnSe have the zinc-blende structure, while BeO and ZnO, among other substances, have the wurtzite structure. The CsCl, NaCl and ZnS co-ordinations are illustrated in Fig. 27.

The purely geometrical account of crystal building which we have given above is of course far too simple, and many other factors have to be taken into account. To mention only

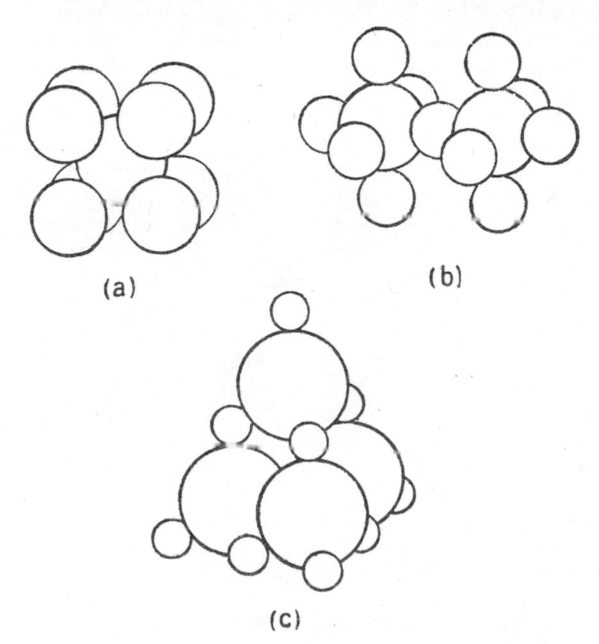

FIG. 27. Types of co-ordination in binary ionic compounds
(*a*) Caesium chloride type
(*b*) Rock-salt type
(*c*) Zinc-blende type

one: if one of the ions is small and the other large and easily polarizable, the polarization forces become considerable and may modify the structure considerably. CdI_2 is an interesting example of this. The crystal is composed of sheets consisting of two layers of the large polarized iodine ions held together by the small cadmium ions between them. Each sheet is very rigid, but adjacent sheets are only lightly held together, and the crystal has a very perfect cleavage.

COMPLEX IONS

Crystals consisting of a metallic ion and a complex ion, such as CO_3, NO_3 or SO_4, have, as a rule, symmetries lower than those of the simple binary compounds, but again the structure appears usually to be determined mainly by the size and shape of the constituent ions. One example of this

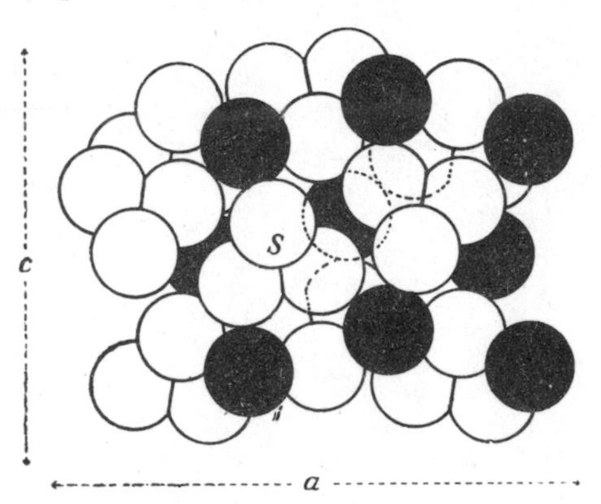

FIG. 28. The barium sulphate structure

The black circles represent the metallic ions, the white circles oxygen, arranged tetrahedrally about sulphur. Only three of the four oxygen atoms in each tetrahedron are visible, the fourth lying immediately below the atoms of type *S*

must suffice. The sulphates of Ba, Sr, and Pb, the perchlorates and permanganates of K, Rb and NH_4, the selenates and chromates of Sr and Ba, and a number of other compounds of the type XRO_4, all crystallize in the same way, forming rather complicated orthorhombic structures (Fig. 28). The reasons for this must be mainly geometrical, for the substances differ greatly chemically, and are alike only in being composed of ions of similar size and shape. The RO_4 group, which consists of a tetrahedral arrangement of O around R, is no doubt the determining factor, but the size of the metallic ion is also of importance, for anhydrite,

$CaSO_4$, with a smaller metallic ion, crystallizes in a different manner. It is perhaps significant that, while the crystals in this series whose ions are univalent are soluble, those in which they are bivalent are in general very insoluble. It seems likely that this is due to the greater forces between the bivalent ions, and illustrates the fact that the physical properties of crystals with similar structures may differ considerably.

THE SILICATES

Some of the gem-stones, and many of the silicates which include a large number of the naturally occurring minerals, are very interesting examples of crystals in which the binding is mainly ionic in character. In these crystals, the most important constituent, oxygen, which is a relatively large ion, is associated with such ions as Si, Al, Be, Mg, and Fe, all of which are considerably smaller. The main bulk of the crystal is occupied by oxygen ions, which are frequently nearly in close-packing, and the smaller ions fit into the spaces between them, acting as a sort of cement to keep the structure together. In the ruby or sapphire, for example, whose formula is Al_2O_3, the oxygen ions are in a hexagonal close-packed array, distorted only slightly by the Al ions which are small enough to fit into its interstices. Olivine, $MgSiO_4$, and chrysoberyl, $BeAl_2O_4$, are also based on a hexagonal close-packed arrangement of oxygen.

The mineral cyanite, Al_2SiO_5, a triclinic crystal, is a very interesting example. The unit cell contains four molecules of cyanite, and therefore 20 atoms of oxygen, which, taking into account the known ionic radius of oxygen in crystals of this type, 1·35 Å, and the size of the unit cell, must be nearly in close-packing. Now it was noticed by W. L. Bragg that, with oxygen atoms in cubic close-packing, it is possible to select a triclinic cell containing 20 atoms, whose size and shape are almost exactly those of the cyanite cell. It appeared likely, therefore, that the structure consisted of a nearly cubic close-packed array of oxygen ions, the low symmetry of the actual crystal being due to the distribution of the Al and Si in the interstices of the structure, an idea whose essential correctness was verified by examining the X-ray spectra given by the crystal. This is an excellent example of the way in which, by taking into account all the circumstances of the case, it is often possible to get at the structure of a crystal far too complicated to yield to a direct attack.

In some of the silicates, the oxygen, while not close-packed throughout the structure, is locally close-packed, forming a kind of girder structure with comparatively wide-open spaces. Beryl, for example, is a honeycomb structure of close-packed oxygen, with actual holes going right through it.

In every silicate that has been analysed, silicon atoms are always found to lie at the centres of a nearly regular tetrahedron composed of four oxygen atoms. In the orthosilicates, these tetrahedra form independent SiO_4 groups, acting as anions in the structure. Other closed groups may also occur, such as Si_2O_7, in which two tetrahedra are linked by a common oxygen atom, or Si_3O_9, which forms a ring of three tetrahedra, and Si_6O_{18} which forms a ring of six. Each of these rings has the composition $(SiO_3)_n$. In some structures, endless chains of tetrahedra, each adjacent pair having a common oxygen atom, are found, and here again, the composition is $(SiO_3)_n$; or two adjacent chains lying side by side may be joined by cross linkages to form endless bands of hexagonal rings, each sharing an edge with those on either side. Such chains and rings are found in fibrous minerals such as asbestos. The tetrahedra may be linked, always through common oxygen atoms, to form sheets of hexagonal rings extending indefinitely in two dimensions, and these are characteristic of flaky minerals such as mica and talc; or, finally, the tetrahedra may form cage-like structures in three dimensions, as in the felspars and zeolites. In all these extended groups certain of the silicon atoms may be replaced by aluminium, which alters the effective valency of the group, and so the possible kations with which it can combine. The extreme variability of the silicates in this respect is thus accounted for. The work of W. L. Bragg and his school in this field has shown clearly that the chemistry of the silicates is a chemistry of the solid state, intelligible only in terms of crystal structure.

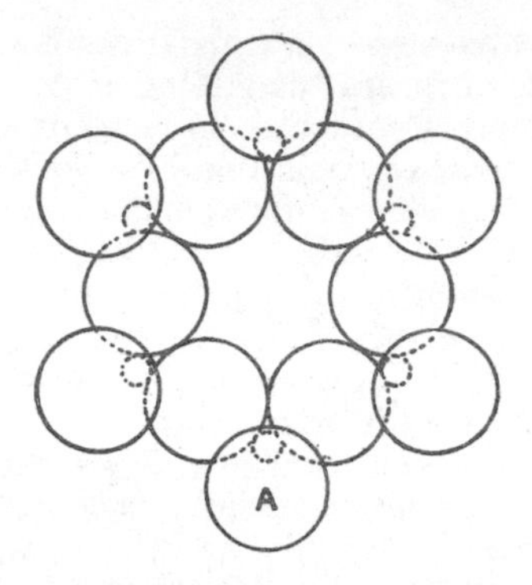

FIG. 29. A ring of SiO_4 groups from the beryl structure

Oxygen atoms are arranged tetrahedrally about the silicon atoms (small dotted circles), the fourth oxygen atom in each tetrahedron being exactly below the atom of type *A*. Each oxygen atom in the ring of six is shared between two silicon atoms. There are six silicon atoms and eighteen oxygen atoms in the ring

MOLECULAR AND ORGANIC CRYSTALS

In the types of structure so far considered, there has been no trace of the chemical molecule. In the rock-salt crystal, for example, each Na atom stands in the same relationship to six Cl atoms, and each Cl atom to six Na atoms, and the whole structure must be considered as a unity. The same is true of the silicate class. Indeed, it may probably be said that, except in the crystalline state, many of the complicated silicates have no distinct existence. In many crystals, however, and particularly in the crystals of the organic compounds, there is a well-defined molecule. The atoms in this molecule are linked together not by ionic or electrostatic forces, but by some form of co-valent binding, such as that which unites two oxygen atoms in the gas molecule, and the whole crystal is built up of such molecules, held together by the residual forces of attraction between them. Such crystals are, as a rule, much softer, far less rigid in structure, and have lower melting-points than the typical ionic crystal.

The study of organic crystals, which started rather later

than that of inorganic ones, has now become one of the most important fields of investigation. One of its earliest results was to show that the structural formulae of organic chemistry did correspond to physical reality. The benzene ring is indeed a ring of six carbon atoms, and the long chain-compounds are really long chains whose length and configuration can be determined, as was shown many years ago by the work of Shearer and Müller on the fatty acids.

The method of Fourier synthesis, described in Chapter V, may be employed with great advantage in the study of organic crystals. One may mention in particular the work of Robertson on aromatic compounds, and on the phthalocyanines, in which by suitably placing a heavy atom in the molecule it was possible to determine the phases of the spectra, and to portray the whole structure in the projection, without even initially assuming anything about it. A more recent and most beautiful example of a full three-dimensional determination of a complicated structure is that of vitamin B_{12} by Dr Dorothy Hodgkin and her collaborators.

Of recent years a large amount of work has been done on biologically interesting substances, and particularly on the proteins. Pioneer work in this field was done many years ago by Astbury in his studies of the fibrous proteins, but more recently a direct attack has been made on the structure of crystalline proteins such as the haemoglobins and myoglobins and the salts of the nucleic acids, by several groups of investigators. This work is of very great difficulty. The crystals contain many thousands of atoms in the unit cell, and usually also liquid of crystallization, either water or solutions of salts, incorporated in the structure, apparently in layers between the more permanent crystalline framework of atoms.

An important step towards the understanding of the proteins was the recognition that they are based on a spiral structure. It was first suggested by Pauling and Corey that the structure of the nucleic-acid chain has a spiral arrangement, and since then considerable progress has been made in the study of the salts of deoxyribose nucleic acid (DNA). Watson and Crick suggested, and later work has confirmed the general correctness of their ideas, that the structure consists of two helical chains, of polypeptide structure, coiled around a common axis. The two chains are held together by purine and pyrimidine bases attached to the sides of the chains, a single base on one chain being linked to single base on the other through a hydrogen bond. The bonding must be between a base of one type on one chain and a base of the other type on the other chain. The bases can be attached to the chain in a variety of ways, and in a great variety of orders, and this gives the possibility of an enormous variability in structures that are yet essentially of the same type.

The fact that a specific pairing of bases on the two chains is necessary means that one helix acts in effect as a template, and can only combine with another having the correct distribution of bases along its length. Watson and Crick made the interesting suggestion that in this kind of process we may perhaps see a copying mechanism for genetic materials.

A helical structure should give a rather characteristic distribution of intensities in an X-ray diffraction pattern, and this is shown by the patterns obtained from the salts of DNA. The detailed structure cannot be yet determined with any certainty.

Crystals of haemoglobin and myoglobin appear to be built of polypeptide chains of this kind, folded in a complex manner, but they contain as well dense flattened disc-like structures, believed to be the haem group with its central iron atom. Quite recently, Kendrew and his fellow workers at Cambridge have succeeded in making a three-dimensional synthesis of sperm-whale myoglobin crystals. They used the method of isomorphous replacement, in which a heavy atom placed in a known position in the structure enables the phases of enough spectra to be determined to make it possible to sum the Fourier series. The resolution obtainable is necessarily low, but a number of the main features of the structure are clearly shown. It is not possible here to give any details of this exceedingly complex work, which constitutes an important advance in the study of the structure of living matter, but a few references are included in the bibliography.

BIBLIOGRAPHY

GENERAL

The Crystalline State, W. H. and W. L. Bragg. Vol. I. A General Survey, by W. L. Bragg (Bell, 1933)

Crystals and X-Rays, Kathleen Lonsdale (Bell, 1948)

Chemical Crystallography, C. W. Bunn (Oxford University Press, 1945)

A Study of Crystal Structure and its Applications, Wheeler P. Davey (McGraw Hill, 1934)

Kristalle und Roentgenstrahlen, P. P. Ewald (Springer, Berlin, 1923)

CHAPTERS I, II, AND III

General Crystallography: *Mineralogy*, H. A. Miers (Macmillan, 1928)

Theory of Space-Groups: *Theorie der Kristallstruktur*, A. Schoenflies (Borntraeger, Berlin, 1923); *Geometrische Kristallographie des Diskontinuums*, P. Niggli (Borntraeger, Leipzig, 1919); *International Tables for X-Ray Crystallography*, published for the International Union of Crystallography (Kynoch Press)

Methods: *X-Ray Crystallography*, M. J. Buerger (Chapman and Hall, 1942); *The Interpretation of X-Ray Diffraction Photographs*, N. F. M. Henry, H. Lipson, and W. A. Wooster (Macmillan, 1951)

CHAPTERS IV AND V

General Physics of X rays, and X-ray optics: *X-Rays in Theory and Experiment*, A. H. Compton and S. K. Allison (Macmillan, 1935); *The Crystalline State*, Vol. II, The Optical Principles of the Diffraction of X-Rays, R. W. James (Bell, 1948); *Roentgenstrahl-Interferenzen*, M. von Laue (Akademische Verlagsgesellschaft, Leipzig, 1948); *Fourier Technique in X-Ray Organic Structure Analysis*, A. D. Booth (Cambridge University Press, 1948); *X-Ray Optics*, A. J. C. Wilson (Methuen's Monographs, 1949)

CHAPTER VI

Structural Inorganic Chemistry, A. F. Wells (Oxford University Press, 1950); *The Atomic Structure of Minerals*, W. L. Bragg (Oxford University Press, 1937); J. M. Robertson, *Journ. Chem. Soc.*, 1936, No. 255, p. 1201; Dorothy Crowfoot Hodgkin *et alia, Proc. Roy. Soc. A*, **242**, 1957, p. 228; J. D. Watson and F. H. C. Crick, *Nature*, 1953, p. 738; Bodo, Dintzis Kendrew and Wyckoff, *Proc. Roy. Soc. A*, 1959, p. 70.

129184

INDEX